REVISE KEY STAGE 2 SATs
Mathematics

REVISION WORKBOOK

Above Expected Standard

Series Consultant: Janice Pimm

Author: Rachel Axten-Higgs

This revision workbook is written for students who aim to perform above the expected national standard in Mathematics in their Year 6 SATs.

For students who hope to perform at the expected standard, check out:

Revise Key Stage 2 SATs Mathematics Revision Guide:
Expected Standard 9781292146263

Revise Key Stage 2 SATs Mathematics Revision Workbook:
Expected Standard 9781292146287

For the full range of Pearson revision titles visit:
www.pearsonschools.co.uk/revise

ALWAYS LEARNING

PEARSON

Contents

Number

Calculation

Fractions, decimals and percentages

Ratio and proportion

Algebra

Measurement

Geometry

Statistics

A small bit of small print

The Standards and Testing Agency publishes Sample Test Materials on its website. This is the official content and this book should be used in conjunction with it. The questions in this book have been written to help you practise what you have learned in your revision. Remember: the real test questions may not look like this.

Introduction

About your tests

At the end of Year 6, you will take tests to find out about your maths skills. This book will help you revise all of the important skills you need for your tests.

- There will be one **arithmetic** test. This test will ask you to carry out calculations. You will have 30 minutes to do this test.
- There will be two **reasoning** tests. These tests will ask you to solve problems. You will have 40 minutes to do each test.

Using this book

Each page of this book is about a different maths skill. Use the checkboxes at the top of the page to track your progress:

Had a look ☐ Tick this box when you've read the page.

Nearly there ☐ Tick this box when you understand the page quite well.

Nailed it! ☐ Tick this box when you understand the page really well.

Place value

1. Write in figures the value of the 9 in each of these numbers.

a) 4,932 ....900...........................

b) 91,014 ......90,000.........................

c) 901,516 ~~9~~ 900,000........................

d) 432,591 ....90..............................

e) 7,592,311 ......90,000.........................

f) 9,501,212 ......90,00,000......................

g) 7,439,520 ....9000...........................   **7 marks**

Say the number out loud to help you.

2. Write in words the place-value column that the 0 is in.
One has been done for you.

a) 1,756,302 ....tens......................

b) 9,201,333 ...Thousands.............................

c) 6,043,521 ..Hundred Thousands.....................

d) 8,970,165 ...Thousands..............................

e) 3,654,097 ...Hundreds................................   **4 marks**

3. Write in figures the value of the underlined digit in each of these numbers.

a) 7,4<u>2</u>1,134 .....20000.............................

b) 4,411,<u>1</u>11 ...100..................................

c) 8,<u>3</u>29,752 ....300 0 00...........................

d) <u>2</u>,213,582 ....2000000............................

e) 6,80<u>1</u>,354 ...1000...............................   **5 marks**

4. Write in figures the difference between the values
of the two underlined digits in each number.

a) 4,<u>6</u>12,<u>6</u>35   600,000 – 600 = 599,400

b) <u>7</u>,<u>7</u>23,469   7,000,000 – 700,000 = 6,300,000

c) <u>5</u>,81<u>5</u>,367   5,000,000 – 5000 = 4,995,000

d) <u>1</u>,283,5<u>1</u>9   1,000,000 – 10 = 999,990.

You can use counting up or written subtraction to find the difference between the values of digits.

3 marks

1

Number lines

1. What is each interval worth on these number lines?

> Count the gaps, not the marks on the line!

a)
```
200                              250
 |  |  |  |  |  |  |  |  |  |  |  |
```
...........5..

b)
```
7.2                              7.3
 |  |  |  |  |  |  |  |  |  |  |  |
```
..........0.01......................................

c)
```
5.6              5.7
 |  |  |  |  |  |
```
.........0.01......................................

d)
```
8.0                              9.0
 |  |  |  |  |  |  |  |  |  |  |  |
```
.........0.1......................................

4 marks

2. Mark the position of 120,325 on each number line.

> Find the size of each interval. Then count up from 120,000

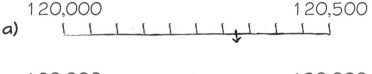

a)
```
120,000                    120,500
   |  |  |  |  |  |  |  |↓ |  |  |  |
```

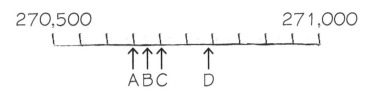

b)
```
120,000                    130,000
   |  |  |  |  |  |  |  |  |  |  |  |
```

2 marks

3. Which of the letters marked on this line represents the number 270,675?

```
270,500                      271,000
   |  |  |  |  |  |  |  |  |  |  |  |
         ↑↑↑      ↑
         ABC      D
```

.........D..

1 mark

Negative numbers

1. Find the difference between the temperatures. Fill in the number lines to help you. One has been done for you.

a) −7°C and 6°C

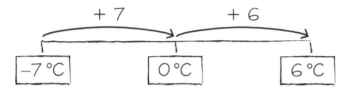

7 + 6 = 13 degrees

b) −12°C and 2°C

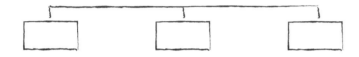

....

c) −3.5°C and 3°C

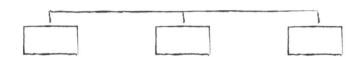

....

2 marks

2. The temperature in Hamburg is 4°C.

a) What temperature is 5 degrees higher than this? ....

b) What temperature is 4.7 degrees lower than this? ....

> To reach a colder temperature, count back from the starting temperature. To reach a warmer temperature, count on from the starting temperature.

2 marks

3. Find the difference between −7.5°C and 3°C.

.... **1 mark**

4. Find the difference between −32.5 and 7.8

.... **1 mark**

3

Number line problems

1. This graph shows the depth in metres of a submarine at eight points during a mission.

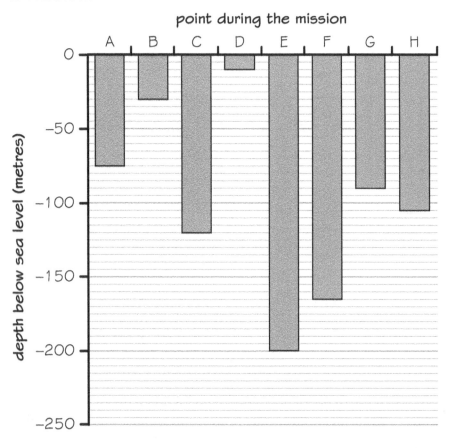

point during the mission

> Work out what each interval on the graph is worth.

Complete the table to show the depth of the submarine at each point during the mission.

point in mission	A	B	C	D	E	F	G	H
depth of submarine	−75 m							

7 marks

2. Use the table to find the difference between these depths.

a) The difference between B and F is .... metres.

b) The difference between A and C is .... metres.

c) The difference between A and H is .... metres.

> You could use written subtraction or you could count the intervals on the graph.

3 marks

Rounding

1. Round 6,723,901 to:

   a) the nearest 10 ....6,723,900..........

   b) the nearest 100 ....

   c) the nearest 1,000 ....

   d) the nearest 10,000 ....

   e) the nearest 100,000 ....

   f) the nearest 1,000,000 ....

   Look at the digit to the right of the place value you are rounding to.

   5 marks

2. Write a number that, when rounded to the nearest 10, would become:

   a) 5,050 ....5,053........   b) 10,870 ....

   c) 432,400 ....   d) 1,067,080 ....

   3 marks

3. Write a number that, when rounded to the nearest 1,000, would become:

   a) 73,000 ......72,692......   b) 103,000 ....

   c) 980,000 ....   d) 910,000 ....

   3 marks

4. Jen is organising a birthday party.
   By rounding the price of each item on her shopping list to the nearest pound, estimate how much she will need to spend on the supplies. Show your working.

   ....

   ....

   ....

   ....

   ....

Shopping list	
Party bags	£15.04
Cake	£18.22
Balloons	£5.63
Paper plates	£3.99
Plastic cutlery	£5.50
Paper cups	£4.49

   4 marks

5

Rounding problems

1. Find the smallest number that rounds to each of these numbers.

   a) 2,430 to the nearest 10   ....

   b) 23,000 to the nearest 1,000   ....

   c) 5,000,000 to the nearest 1,000,000   ....

   > Subtract half of the number you are rounding to. If you are rounding to the nearest 100, subtract 50

   3 marks

2. Find the largest whole number that rounds to each of these numbers.

   a) 1,300 to the nearest 100   ....

   b) 260,000 to the nearest 10,000   ....

   c) 800,000 to the nearest 100,000   ....

   > Add half of the number you are rounding to and then take away 1

   3 marks

3. Write the smallest and largest whole numbers that would round to these numbers when rounding to 1,000. One has been done for you.

   a) 67,000   smallest: ......**66,500**......   largest: ....**67,499**..........

   b) 345,000   smallest: ....   largest: ....

   c) 2,340,000   smallest: ....   largest: ....

   2 marks

4. Write the largest and smallest whole numbers that would round to the central numbers.

   a) Rounding to the nearest 1,000

☐ ←	78,000	→ ☐
smallest		largest

   b) Rounding to the nearest 100,000

☐ ←	600,000	→ ☐
smallest		largest

   2 marks

Roman numerals

1. Complete the table to show the values of the Roman numerals.
   One has been done for you.

I	V	X	L	C	D	M
		10				

   > Make sure you learn the value of each of these letters.

   6 marks

2. Write the value of each of these Roman numerals.

   > If one or more letters are written **after** another letter of greater value, add that amount. If I, X or C is written **before** another letter of greater value, subtract that amount.

   a) III   ....

   b) LV   ....

   c) DL   ....

   d) MCDXCVIII   ....

   4 marks

3. Write each of these numbers using Roman numerals.

   a) 84   ....   b) 247   ....

   c) 854   ....   d) 3,012   ....

   4 marks

4. Complete these calculations. Write your answers in figures.

   a) DCC – LXXX = ...

   b) MMDC + MXCIX = ...

   c) MMMDCCC – CM = ... **3 marks**

5. The distance between London and New York is MMMCDLVIII miles.
   Write this distance in numbers.

   .... **1 mark**

Addition

1. Answer these additions mentally.

> How many 10,000s does 30,400 have? How many 100s?

a) 867,531 + 30,400 = ...

> Add 0.2 to get to the next whole number. How much more do you have to add?

b) 156.8 + 0.7 = ...

> What number could you add on instead of 499? How would you need to adjust your answer?

c) 756,281 + 499 = ...

3 marks

2. Use written column addition to complete these calculations.

a) 256,832 + 1,603,021

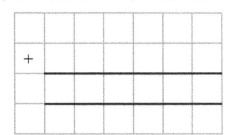

b) 4,300,106 + 801,900

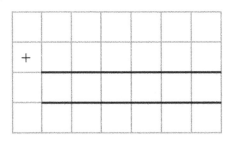

> Line up the digits and decimal points carefully before you add.

c) 943.76 + 1.044

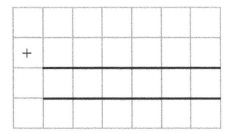

d) 1,985.91 + 222.23

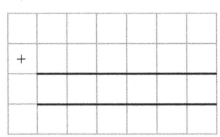

4 marks

8

Subtraction

1. Complete these subtractions mentally.

> How many 10,000s are in 40,303? How many hundreds? How many units?

a) 257,635 − 40,303 = ...

> Try counting up from 1,080 to 65,000

b) 65,000 − 1,080 = ...

> What number could you subtract instead of 19.9 to make this easier? How would you need to adjust your answer?

c) 456.8 − 19.9 = ...

3 marks

2. Use written column subtraction to complete these calculations.

> Don't forget to use zeros in empty place value columns.

a) 6,678,203 − 345,268

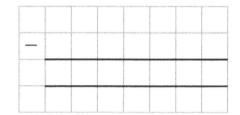

b) 3,456,005 − 1,609,893

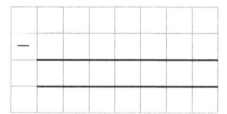

c) 365.89 − 57.95

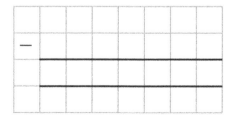

d) 89.5 − 6.903

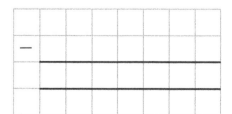

4 marks

9

Add/subtract problems

1. Last year, Tobias travelled 15,672 miles in his car. The year before, he travelled 2,094 miles less. How many miles did he travel in his car over the two years?

> Remember the acronym RNCA to help you with multi-step problems. Read the question, Note the important information, Calculate, write your Answer.

....   **2 marks**

2. Mrs Ashraf bought some new school uniform for her son Bilal. She spent a total of £50.36 on two pairs of shorts, a shirt, a jumper and a pack of socks. The shorts cost £8.99 each, the jumper cost £16.60 and the pack of socks cost £4.29.

   How much did the shirt cost?

....   **2 marks**

3. In her science class, Jenny mixes 145.5 ml of one liquid with 16.2 ml of another. She then pours away 12.8 ml of the liquid and adds 150.0 ml of water.

   How much liquid is in the finished mixture in total?

....   **2 marks**

Multiples

1. On this grid, the multiples of 2 have been circled in grey.

   Circle the multiples of 3, 6 and 10

   Use a different colour for each set of multiples.

1	②	3	④	5	⑥	7	⑧	9	⑩
11	⑫	13	⑭	15	⑯	17	⑱	19	⑳
21	㉒	23	㉔	25	㉖	27	㉘	29	㉚

   3 marks

2. List the common multiples of 3 and 6. Use the grid above to help you.

   ....

   5 marks

3. Sasha says that 4,500 is a multiple of 90. Is she correct?
   Explain how you know.

   ....

   ....

   ....   **2 marks**

4. Circle the numbers that are multiples of 7

   56   107   112   201   217   300   392   892   1,400   1,700

   5 marks

5. A biscuit factory packages its biscuits into packs of 16

   Can 29,173 biscuits be packaged so that each pack is full and no biscuits
   are left over? Explain your answer.

   ....

   ....

   ....   **2 marks**

Factors

1. List all of the factors of each number.

   a) 18 ....

   b) 34 ....

   c) 64 ....

   d) 78 ....   **4 marks**

2. Write the common factors of 9, 45 and 90

   ....

   ....

   ....

   ....   **2 marks**

   > Write down all the factors for each number. Then look for the factors that appear in all three lists.

3. A toy shop is celebrating its fifth birthday. Every fourth customer receives a free kite, and every fifth customer receives a free stuffed toy. How many customers will the shop have had by the time someone receives both free gifts?

   ....

   ....

   ....

   ....

   ....   **2 marks**

   > What is the lowest number that has the factors 4 and 5?

Prime numbers

1. Write all the prime numbers up to 50

.... 5 marks

2. Write each of these numbers as a multiplication using its prime factors. One has been done for you.

a) 18 = ...**2 × 3 × 3**......   b) 30 = ...

c) 34 = ...   d) 46 = ...

e) 49 = ...   f) 78 = ... 5 marks

3. Circle the prime numbers. One has been done for you.

    55   61   97   (101)   103   126   139   163   194   199

                                                     5 marks

4. Is the number 307 prime? How do you know? Show your working.

....

....

....

> Start by testing whether 307 divides by 2, then try the other prime numbers to see if 307 has any factors.

                                              2 marks

5. Write a multiplication using only prime numbers that has the answer 70

....

....

....

> First, find any two numbers that multiply to make 70. Keep finding pairs of numbers that multiply to make one of these until all of the numbers are prime.

                                              1 mark

Squares and cubes

1. Write the square numbers that these diagrams show.
   One has been done for you.

   a)    b) 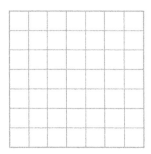   c)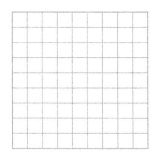

   .....6 × 6 = 36.....   ....

   2 marks

2. Write the value of each of these square numbers.

   a) $8^2 =$ ....   b) $11^2 =$ ....   c) $15^2 =$ ....

   3 marks

3. Write the cube numbers that these diagrams show.
   One has been done for you.

   a) 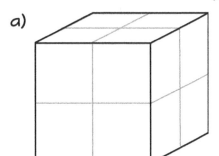   b) 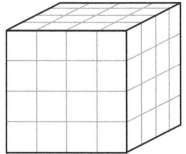   c)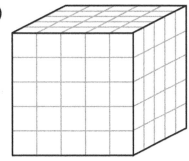

   .....2 × 2 × 2 = 8.....   ....

   2 marks

4. Here is a list of numbers.

   | 25 | 64 | 88 | 216 | 343 | 999 | 216,000 |

   a) Circle the cube numbers.

   b) Write each of the cube numbers above using the cubed symbol.

   ....

   4 marks

Moving digits

1. Show what happens to these numbers when they are multiplied by the number given. Write the new number and draw arrows to show how the digits have moved. One has been done for you.

   a) Multiply by 10

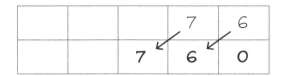

   b) Multiply by 100

   c) Multiply by 100

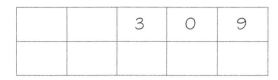

   d) Multiply by 1,000

   3 marks

2. Divide each of these numbers by 10 and 1,000

   a) $6,457 \div 10 =$ .... $6,457 \div 1,000 =$ ....

   b) $11,856 \div 10 =$ .... $11,856 \div 1,000 =$ ....

   c) $654.73 \div 10 =$ .... $654.73 \div 1,000 =$ ....

   6 marks

3. Zena earns 75p for each length of the swimming pool she swims. She swims 100 lengths in total. How much does she earn?

   First decide whether you need to multiply or divide.

   ....

   ....

   1 mark

4. Henry pays £247 for him and 9 friends to visit a safari park. How much does each person's ticket cost?

   ....

   ....

   1 mark

Multiplication

1. Use short multiplication to find the answers to these calculations. One has been done for you.

> Leave space under the answer to carry digits.

a) 567 × 9

```
    5 6 7
×       9
─────────
  5 1 0 3
    6 6
```

.....**5,103**.....

b) 708 × 4

....

c) 5,641 × 3

....

2 marks

2. Use long multiplication to find the answers to these calculations. One has been done for you.

a) 215 × 32

```
      2 1 5
×       3 2
───────────
    6 4̄5 0
      4 3̄0
───────────
    6 8 8 0
```

.....**6,880**.....

b) 856 × 75

....

c) 1,034 × 57

....

4 marks

3. Shaun is organising a party and needs to buy enough fizzy drinks for all of his guests. He decides to buy 660 ml per person. He has 21 guests. Use long multiplication to work out how many millilitres of fizzy drinks he needs to buy in total.

....   **2 marks**

Division

1. Answer these calculations using short division. Give any remainders as decimals. One has been done for you.

   a) 6,392 ÷ 5   **b)** 7,035 ÷ 8   **c)** 9,003 ÷ 4

   ```
        1 2 7 8 . 4
     5 | 6 ¹3 ³9 ⁴2 . ²0
   ```

   2 marks

2. Answer these calculations using long division. Write any remainders using the letter 'r' and a whole number. One has been done for you.

   a) 8,962 ÷ 32   **b)** 8,032 ÷ 48

   First multiples of 32 =   First multiples of 48 =

   <u>32, 64, 96, 128,</u>   ....

   <u>160, 192, 224, 256</u>   ....

   ```
           2 8 0  r 2
     32 | 8 9 6 2
          6 4 0 0   (32 × 200)
          2 5 6 2
          2 5 6 0   (32 × 80)
                2
   ```

   2 marks

3. Joel works in a sweet shop. He has a large jar of 3,570 g of wine gums and has to share them into 35 g bags. How many bags of sweets can he make?

   .... **2 marks**

17

Remainders

1. A school buys packs of 72 pencils.
   There are 358 children in the school.
   How many packs should the school buy
   so that each child in the school can
   be given one pencil?

> Read the problems carefully. Round the remainders so they make sense in the context of the question.

.... **2 marks**

2. Ice lollies are sold in packs of 12. Peter wants 170 ice lollies to sell to people at a fair. How many packs does Peter need to buy?

.... **2 marks**

3. A group of 9 friends are on a skiing holiday.

   a) Their ski hire costs a total of £506.99.
      If they divide it fairly among themselves,
      how much will each friend pay?

.... **2 marks**

   b) How much change will the group receive?

.... **1 mark**

Multi-step problems

1. Freddie has an animal magazine delivered to him every month for a year. He pays £58.19 a year for the magazine. This includes one free issue.

   > Don't forget to use RNCA (Read, Note information, Calculate, Answer) to help you answer multi-step questions.

   a) How much does each issue cost?

   .... **2 marks**

   b) How much would it cost for the year if one issue was not free?

   .... **1 mark**

2. Rhea and James are raising money for charity by doing a sponsored book read.
   Rhea will raise 82p for each book she reads.
   James will raise £1.20 for each book he reads.
   If they each read 20 books, how much money will they raise in total?

   > What calculations do you need to do – add, subtract, multiply or divide?

   .... **2 marks**

3. In a gymnastics competition, Scarlett is awarded 84 points for her routine. Freya is awarded twice as many points as Scarlett. Oscar is awarded 16 points fewer than Freya. How many points do the children receive altogether?

   .... **2 marks**

Order of operations

1. Complete the calculations.

   a) $88 \div 8 \times (5 - 2) =$ ....

   b) $(8 + 24) \div (8 - 4) =$ ....

   c) $5 \times 7 + 23 - 6 =$ ....

   d) $28 + 33 - 6 \times 7 =$ ....

   e) $17 \times 6 - 20 \div (2 + 2) =$ ....

   f) $7 \times 5 - 6 \div 2 =$ ....

   > Do any multiplication and division first unless there are brackets.

   3 marks

2. Find the answers to the questions in each pair. Then find the difference between them.

   a) $(7 \times 2) + (12 \div 3) =$ .... $7 \times (2 + 12) \div 3 =$ ....

   difference = ...

   b) $6 \times 4 - 6 + 8 =$ .... $6 \times 4 - (6 + 8) =$ ....

   difference = ...   **6 marks**

3. Add brackets to make the following statements true.

   a) $7 + 3 \times 5 \div 1 + 4 = 10$

   b) $10 + 30 \div 15 + 5 = 2$

   c) $12 + 9 \div 3 + 3 = 10$ **3 marks**

4. Dmitri had £54. Adam was given £84.76 for Christmas. Adam gave £20 to charity and then gave half his remaining money to Dmitri. Write a calculation using brackets that shows how much Dmitri has now. Then work out the answer.

   ....

   ....   **2 marks**

Solving problems

1. Use inverse operations to solve these problems.

a) Lotta thinks of a number less than 150. She multiplies it by 3, then adds 69. She divides the result by 4. Her answer is 105. What number did she start with?

> Start with Lotta's answer and work backwards.

....

....

....

b) Jonah starts with a number between 200 and 300
He divides it by 2 and then adds 64
He multiplies the result by 2. His answer is 353
What was the number he started with?

....

....

....

4 marks

2. Write the missing digits to make these calculations correct.

a)

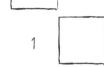

```
      □  2
 ×    1  □
 ─────────
   2  0  8
   5  2  0
 ─────────
   7  2  8
```

b)

```
      8  □
 ×    □  3
 ─────────
   2  4  9
 1  6  6  0
 ─────────
 1  9  0  9
```

> You can use inverse operations to find the missing numbers. What do you need to multiply by 10 to get 520?

4 marks

Equivalent fractions

1. Work out the missing numbers to complete the pairs of equivalent fractions.

a) $\dfrac{4}{5} = \dfrac{\square}{20}$

b) $\dfrac{3}{9} = \dfrac{\square}{45}$

c) $\dfrac{9}{11} = \dfrac{54}{\square}$

d) $\dfrac{14}{21} = \dfrac{\square}{3}$

e) $\dfrac{3}{24} = \dfrac{1}{\square}$

f) $\dfrac{6}{7} = \dfrac{30}{\square}$

5 marks

2. Draw lines to match the pairs of equivalent fractions.

$\dfrac{5}{7}$ $\dfrac{1}{4}$ $\dfrac{2}{3}$ $\dfrac{8}{13}$ $\dfrac{3}{8}$

> To find an equivalent fraction, multiply or divide the numerator and denominator by the same number.

$\dfrac{44}{66}$ $\dfrac{27}{72}$ $\dfrac{45}{63}$ $\dfrac{40}{160}$ $\dfrac{16}{26}$

5 marks

3. Circle all of the fractions that are equivalent to $\dfrac{7}{8}$

$\dfrac{21}{32}$ $\dfrac{14}{21}$ $\dfrac{32}{36}$ $\dfrac{35}{40}$ $\dfrac{58}{65}$ $\dfrac{63}{72}$

1 mark

4. Write 5 fractions that are equivalent to $\dfrac{12}{16}$

....

5 marks

Simplest form

1. Use the common factor given to simplify each of these fractions.

> To simplify a fraction, divide both the numerator and denominator by a common factor to find an equivalent fraction.

a) Common factor 12 $\dfrac{48}{60}$ = ...

b) Common factor 25 $\dfrac{75}{125}$ = ...

c) Common factor 4 $\dfrac{52}{72}$ = ...

d) Common factor 6 $\dfrac{54}{78}$ = ...

e) Common factor 7 $\dfrac{49}{77}$ = ...

5 marks

2. Simplify these fractions.
   Continue until you reach the simplest form, and draw a circle round it.
   One has been done for you.

> Keep dividing the numerator and denominator by common factors until there are no common factors left.

a) $\dfrac{16}{40}$ = $\dfrac{16 \div 4}{40 \div 4} = \dfrac{4}{10} = \dfrac{4 \div 2}{10 \div 2} = \boxed{\dfrac{2}{5}}$ ....

b) $\dfrac{27}{63}$ = ...

c) $\dfrac{65}{160}$ = ...

d) $\dfrac{30}{598}$ = ...

e) $\dfrac{306}{408}$ = ...

f) $\dfrac{273}{378}$ = ...

5 marks

Ordering fractions

1. Convert these improper fractions to mixed numbers in their simplest form. One has been done for you.

   a) $\dfrac{21}{6} = \dfrac{18}{6} + \dfrac{3}{6} = 3\dfrac{1}{2}$ b) $\dfrac{17}{4} =$ ....

   c) $\dfrac{35}{12} =$ ....   d) $\dfrac{72}{5} =$ ....

3 marks

2. Convert these mixed numbers to improper fractions. One has been done for you.

   a) $5\dfrac{3}{8} = \dfrac{43}{8}$ ....   b) $3\dfrac{9}{11} =$ ....

   c) $2\dfrac{13}{17} =$ ....   d) $8\dfrac{5}{7} =$ ....   3 marks

3. Write these fractions in order from smallest to largest.

   a) $9\dfrac{3}{4}$ $\dfrac{9}{12}$ $\dfrac{23}{4}$

   > Change any mixed numbers to fractions, then find equivalent fractions all with the same denominator before you compare them.

   ....

   b) $\dfrac{17}{3}$ $\dfrac{30}{6}$ $5\dfrac{3}{12}$

   .... 4 marks

Add/subtract fractions

1. Change each set of fractions to equivalent
   fractions with the same denominator,
   then add all three fractions.
   Write your answer as a mixed number.

   > Once all three fractions have the same denominator, add the numerators. The denominator stays the same.

   a) $\dfrac{7}{12}$ = ... $\dfrac{2}{3}$ = ... $\dfrac{5}{6}$ = ...

   total = ...

   b) $\dfrac{6}{9}$ = ... $\dfrac{5}{3}$ = ... $\dfrac{4}{18}$ = ...

   total = ...

   c) $\dfrac{8}{2}$ = ... $\dfrac{9}{15}$ = ... $\dfrac{7}{10}$ = ...

   total = ...   **6 marks**

2. Solve these calculations. Write your answers as improper fractions in their
   simplest form.

   a) $\dfrac{9}{4} - \dfrac{7}{12}$

   b) $7\dfrac{8}{10} - 5\dfrac{4}{2}$

   ....

   c) $5\dfrac{6}{9} + \dfrac{12}{3}$

   ....   **3 marks**

25

Multiplying fractions

1. Multiply the fraction $\frac{4}{7}$ by the following whole numbers. Write your answers as mixed numbers.

> To multiply a fraction by a whole number, multiply the numerator by the whole number and keep the denominator the same.

   a) 3 = ...

   b) 5 = ...

   c) 8 = ...

   d) 9 = ...

   e) 13 = ...   **5 marks**

2. Mrs Boyd runs a bakery. She makes 6 cakes. She cuts each cake into 8 slices. She takes 3 slices from each cake for her assorted boxes. How many cakes does she have left to sell? Write your answer as a mixed number.

                                                  ....   **2 marks**

3. Solve these multiplications. Write your answers in their simplest form. Change any improper fractions to mixed numbers.

> To multiply two fractions multiply the numerators, then multiply the denominators.

   a) $\frac{3}{7} \times \frac{4}{3}$ = ...

   b) $\frac{3}{4} \times \frac{11}{2}$ = ...

   c) $\frac{4}{7} \times \frac{6}{9}$ = ...

   d) $\frac{7}{9} \times \frac{9}{7}$ = ...   **8 marks**

Dividing fractions

1. Complete these divisions.

   a) $\dfrac{1}{8} \div 5 =$ ....

   b) $\dfrac{3}{5} \div 3 =$ ....

   c) $\dfrac{8}{9} \div 7 =$ ....

   > To divide a fraction by a whole number, multiply the denominator of the fraction by the whole number.

   3 marks

2. Tony makes a pie. He cuts it into 12 portions and eats 2 of them.
   He divides the rest of the pie between five of his friends.
   What fraction of the pie does each friend get?
   Write your answer in its simplest form.

   .... **2 marks**

3. A group of 12 friends share 3 pizzas. They cut each pizza into 16 slices.

   What fraction of one whole pizza does each friend get?

   Write your answer in its simplest form.

   .... **3 marks**

4. Use inverse multiplication to solve each of these calculations.

   a) $\dfrac{4}{8} \div 6 =$ ....

   b) $\dfrac{3}{9} \div 5 =$ ....

   c) $\dfrac{2}{5} \div 9 =$ ....

   > Dividing by 6 is the same as multiplying by $\dfrac{1}{6}$

   3 marks

Decimals

1. Write the value of each underlined digit. One has been done for you.

   a) 29.<u>6</u>43 ......6 tenths......

   b) 34.<u>7</u>89 ....

   c) 74.03<u>1</u> ....

   d) <u>3</u>9.003 ....

3 marks

2. Convert these fractions into decimals.

   a) $\dfrac{5}{10}$ = ...

   b) $\dfrac{9}{100}$ = ...

   c) $\dfrac{7}{1000}$ = ...

   d) $\dfrac{64}{100}$ = ...

   e) $\dfrac{568}{1000}$ = ...

   f) $\dfrac{403}{1000}$ = ...

   > If the denominator is 10, 100 or 1,000, think about the place value when converting to a decimal.

6 marks

3. Convert these fractions into decimals.
   One has been done for you.

   a) $\dfrac{3}{5}$ = ...$\dfrac{6}{10}$...... = ...0.6......

   b) $\dfrac{14}{20}$ = ... = ...

   c) $\dfrac{17}{50}$ = ... = ...

   d) $\dfrac{385}{500}$ = ... = ...

   e) $\dfrac{18}{25}$ = ... = ...

   > First find an equivalent fraction with a denominator of 10, 10 or 1,000

8 marks

Fractions and decimals

1. Use written division to find the decimal equivalents of these fractions. One has been done for you.

a) $\dfrac{6}{8}$

$$8\overline{\smash{)}6\,.{}^{6}0\,{}^{4}0} \quad\begin{array}{r}0\,.\,7\,5\end{array}$$

......0.75......

> Divide the numerator by the denominator.

b) $\dfrac{7}{16}$

....

c) $\dfrac{3}{8}$

....

d) $\dfrac{9}{16}$

....

3 marks

2. Use written division to find the decimal equivalents of these fractions. Round the recurring decimals to 3 decimal places.

a) $\dfrac{5}{9}$

....

b) $\dfrac{3}{9}$

....

c) $\dfrac{4}{6}$

....

3 marks

3. Tom planted 36 plants. The flowers of each plant were either purple or red. 27 of the plants had purple flowers.

a) What fraction of the plants had red flowers?   ....

> Use the space for your written division.

b) What is this fraction as a decimal?   ....   **3 marks**

Rounding decimals

1. Round these decimals to the nearest whole number.

   a) 4.678 ....

   b) 7.309 ....

   c) 9.888 ....

   d) 20.76 ....   **4 marks**

2. Round these decimals to 1 decimal place.

   a) 7.894   ....

   b) 12.678   ....

   c) 134.608 ....

   d) 22.558   ....

   > Always look at the digit to the right of the place value you are rounding to. If it is 5 or more, round up. If it is lower than 5, round down.

   4 marks

3. Round these decimals to 2 decimal places.

   a) 23.987   ....

   b) 88.888   ....

   c) 70.007   ....

   d) 112.112 ....   **4 marks**

4. Write the smallest and largest numbers with 2 decimal places that would round to these numbers when rounded to 1 decimal place. One has been done for you.

   > To find the smallest number, subtract 0.05 To find the largest number, add 0.04

   a) 98.7   smallest: ....98.65.....   largest: ....98.74.....

   b) 101.4   smallest: ....   largest: ....

   c) 0.9   smallest: ....   largest: ....   **4 marks**

Multiplying decimals

1. Work out these multiplications. Start by multiplying the decimal by a power of 10 to make it easier. One has been done for you.

> Divide the answer by the same power of 10 that you multiplied the decimal by.

a) 0.7×8

Multiply the decimal by ...**10**... to get ...**7**...   **7** $\times 8 =$ **56**

Divide the answer by ...**10**... to get **5.6** $0.7 \times 8 =$ **5.6**

b) 0.03×7

Multiply the decimal by .... to get .... $\times 7 =$ ....

Divide the answer by .... to get .... $0.03 \times 7 =$ ....

c) 2.4×9

Multiply the decimal by .... to get .... $\times 9 =$ ....

Divide the answer by .... to get .... $2.4 \times 9 =$ ....

2 marks

2. Mr Beattie gives £0.56 to charity every week for 18 weeks. How much money does he give to charity in total?

> Use a power of 10 to help you solve this problem.

....   **2 marks**

3. The children at a school run around a running track 9 times. Each lap is 0.18 km. How far does each child run in total?

....   **2 marks**

Percentages

1. On each grid, shade the percentage shown.
   Write the equivalent fraction in its simplest form next to each percentage.

   a) 86% = ...

   b) 47% = ...

   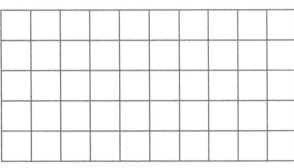 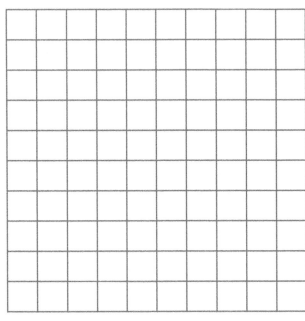

   c) 30% = ...

   d) 75% = ...

4 marks

2. Chad uses blue, green and red bricks to make a model. 20% of the bricks are blue. $\frac{2}{5}$ of the bricks are red. What percentage of the bricks are green?

   ....

   .... 2 marks

3. A bag of counters contains blue, red, green and white counters. $\frac{3}{4}$ of the counters are red. $\frac{1}{10}$ are white. There are the same number of blue counters and green counters. What percentage of the counters are blue?

   ....

   .... 2 marks

Percentages and decimals

1. Change these decimals to percentages.

   a) 0.65 = ...

   b) 0.6 = ...

   > Multiply a decimal by 100 to change it to a percentage.

   c) 0.07 = ...

   d) 0.085 = ...

   4 marks

2. Change these percentages to decimals.

   a) 87% = ...

   b) 48% = ...

   c) 30% = ...

   d) 29% = ...   **4 marks**

3. Raoul travels a distance of 100m. He walks for 0.3 of the total distance, skips for 25% of the distance and jogs for the remaining part of the distance.

   a) What distance, as a percentage, does he walk for? ....

   b) What distance, as a decimal, does he skip for? ....

   c) What distance, as a decimal, does he jog for? ....

   3 marks

4. Matilda has a 1kg bar of chocolate. She gives 40% of it to her cousin, and 0.3 of it to a friend. Matilda then saves 15% for later and eats the rest.

   a) How much did she give her cousin (as a decimal)? ....

   b) How much did she give her friend (as a percentage)? ....

   c) How much did she save for later (as a decimal)? ....

   d) How much did she eat? Give your answer as a decimal and as a percentage.

   ....

   ....   **5 marks**

Equivalence

1. Sam needs to change 0.73 into a percentage.
   Write an explanation of how to do this, and work out the answer.

   ....

   .... **2 marks**

2. Lizzie needs to change $\frac{4}{5}$ into a percentage.

   Write an explanation of how to do this, and work out the answer.

   ....

   .... **2 marks**

3. Maelin wants to change 94% into a fraction.
   Write an explanation of how to do this, and work out the answer.

   ....

   ....

   .... **2 marks**

4. Write these percentages as decimals and as fractions in their simplest forms.

   a) 67%   decimal: ....   fraction: ....

   b) 79%   decimal: ....   fraction: ....

   c) 8%   decimal: ....   fraction: ....

   d) 15%   decimal: ....   fraction: ....

   4 marks

5. Write these decimals as percentages and as fractions in their simplest forms.

   a) 0.07   percentage: ....   fraction: ....

   b) 0.16   percentage: ....   fraction: ....

   c) 0.10   percentage: ....   fraction: ....

   d) 0.40   percentage: ....   fraction: ....

   4 marks

Fraction problems

1. Zainab has a piece of string that is 88 cm long. She divides the string into two pieces. One is $\frac{5}{12}$ of the total length and the other is $\frac{7}{12}$. How long is the shorter of the two new pieces of string? Give your answer to 2 decimal places.

....

.... **1 mark**

2. Children are running around an athletics track. One lap is 400 m in total. Ewan manages to run only $\frac{4}{9}$ of a lap. How far does Ewan run in metres? Give your answer to 2 decimal places.

....

.... **1 mark**

3. A cake weighs 850 g. A group of friends eat $\frac{6}{9}$ of the cake.

   How much do they eat in total in grams?

   Give your answer to 2 decimal places.

   > To find a fraction of a number, multiply by the numerator and divide by the denominator.

....

.... **2 marks**

4. Three types of dried fruit are added to a fruit cake mixture:
   33 g of cherries, 0.067 kg of sultanas, and 0.15 kg of raisins.
   The cake ingredients weigh 750 g in total.
   What fraction of the cake is dried fruit?
   Write your answer in its simplest form.

   > Convert all the quantities to the same units before adding.

....

.... **2 marks**

Finding percentages

1. What is 40% of 600? Show your working.

> 40% is the same as 0.4

....

.... **2 marks**

2. What is 27% of £2,300? Show your working.

> You could work out 25% and then add on two lots of 1%

....

....

.... **2 marks**

3. Natasha receives £123 for her birthday. She uses 55% of the money to book tickets for a concert. How much has she spent on the tickets?

....

.... **2 marks**

4. Jonah enters a 1,500 m charity race. He walks for 12% of the distance and runs for 88%. How far does he run? Show your working.

....

.... **2 marks**

5. Amelie wants to make a cake. She needs 680 g of flour, but she only has 91% of this amount. How much flour does Amelie have? Show your working.

> You could work out 9 lots of 10%, and add on 1%.

....

.... **2 marks**

Ratio and proportion

1. What proportion of each diagram is shaded grey?
   Write each answer as a fraction, a decimal and a percentage.

   a)

   fraction: ....   decimal: ....   percentage: ....

   b)

   fraction: ....   decimal: ....   percentage: ....

   c)

   fraction: ....   decimal: ....   percentage: ....

   3 marks

2. For each of the diagrams shown in question 1,
   write the ratio of grey to white. Write each
   answer in its simplest form.

   > Remember to write the grey number first and the white number second.

   a) ....

   b) ....

   c) ....   **3 marks**

3. Write each of these ratios in its simplest form.

   a) 6:9 = ...   b) 2:10 = ...

   c) 4:8 = ...   d) 12:4 = ...   **4 marks**

4. Write 3 ratios that are equivalent to the ratio 6:2

   ....   **3 marks**

Unequal sharing

1. In a school, there is 1 member of staff for every 6 children. The school employs 55 members of staff. How many children are in the school?

....

.... **1 mark**

2. For every 50p Sebastian collects for charity, his parents give £3.

   a) Write the ratio for this arrangement.

   ....

   ....

   > Make sure both amounts are in the same units before you write the ratio.

   b) If Sebastian raises £3.50 for charity, how much do his parents give?

   ....

   .... **2 marks**

3. In a cake mixture the ratio of wet ingredients to dry ingredients is 3 : 7 The total amount of mixture is 875 g.

   a) How many grams of wet ingredients are there?

   ....

   ....

   b) How many grams of dry ingredients are there?

   ....

   .... **2 marks**

Ratio problems

1. On a sheet of stickers, there are 3 red stickers for every 8 blue stickers. There are 15 red stickers on the sheet. How many blue stickers are there?

....

.... **2 marks**

2. Ulrika mixes 3 parts orange paint with 5 parts green paint. She uses 450 ml of green paint. How much orange paint does she need?

> Divide the amount of green paint by how many parts it represents to find out how much paint is 1 part. Then multiply by the number of parts of orange paint.

....

.... **2 marks**

3. A biscuit factory puts two different shapes of biscuits into its packs. For every 6 round biscuits, there are 3 square biscuits. The largest pack they sell contains 27 square biscuits. How many round biscuits are there in this pack?

....

.... **2 marks**

4. Ali wants to make a strawberry milkshake. The recipe says he needs 9 parts milk to 2 parts strawberry mix. Ali has 90 ml of strawberry mix.

   a) How much milk does Ali need?

   ....

   .... **2 marks**

   b) How many millilitres of milkshake does he make in total?

   ....

   .... **1 mark**

39

Scaling

1. Here are pictures of three scale models. Work out the dimensions of the real objects using the scale factors shown. Write your answers in metres.

a)

64 cm

25 cm

scale factor = 500 : 1

width = ...

height = ...

b)

0.9 cm

14.3 cm

scale factor = 2,000 : 1

width = ...

height = ...

4 marks

2. Sven drew a plan of his bedroom. He used the scale 2 cm to 4 m. Measure the diagram and write on the plan the actual length of each wall in metres.

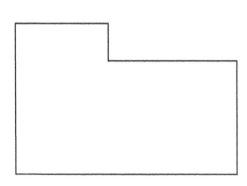

> 2 cm to 4 m is a ratio of 1 cm : 2 m. Multiply the number of centimetres by 2 to find the number of metres.

6 marks

Similarity

1. On the grid, draw a similar shape that is an enlargement of the given shape.

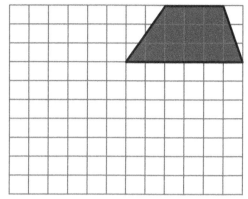

> Use a ruler or count the squares to make sure your new shape is similar to the given one.

2 marks

2. Rectangle A has length 12 cm and width 3.9 cm

   a) Rectangle A is similar to a smaller rectangle of length 4 cm. What is the width of the smaller rectangle?

   ....

   .... **1 mark**

   b) Rectangle A is also similar to a larger rectangle of length 36 cm. What is the width of this larger rectangle?

   ....

   .... **1 mark**

3. A triangle has sides of 2.5 cm, 4.5 cm and 7 cm
   It is enlarged by a scale factor of 5
   Write the lengths of the 3 sides of the new triangle.

   > Multiply each length by the scale factor to find the new lengths.

   .... **3 marks**

41

Using letters

1. Find the value of the letter in each of these addition and subtraction equations.

   a) $17 - b = 6$ $b =$ ....

   b) $12 + d = 21$ $d =$ ....

   c) $16 - z = 4.5$ $z =$ ....

   d) $8.5 - f = -2$ $f =$ ....

   > Use inverse operations to help you solve equations.

   4 marks

2. Find the value of the letters in each of these multiplication and division equations.

   a) $5 \times f = 60$ $f =$ ....   b) $8 \times j = 24$ $j =$ ....

   c) $84 \div h = 14$ $h =$ ....   d) $12 \times k = 156$ $k =$ ....

   4 marks

3. Find the value of each letter in these equations.

   a) $r \div 6 = 32$ $r =$ ....

   b) $13 \times y = 208$ $y =$ ....

   c) $(z + 12) \div 6 = 6$ $z =$ ....

   d) $3 \times (p + 11) = 198$ $p =$ ....

   > Remember the order of operations when working with brackets. Work backwards through the calculation.

   4 marks

4. Sophia thinks of a number. She adds 17 and then divides by 2 The answer is 8. What is the number Sophia thought of?

   ....

   ....   **1 mark**

5. Rohan spends £2.70 on a birthday card. He spends £10.54 on a present. Then he spends half of his remaining money on lunch. Rohan now has £6.34 How much did he have to begin with?

   ....

   ....   **1 mark**

Simple formulae

1. The total cost of hiring a pedal boat is worked out by multiplying the number of minutes it is hired for (m) by the cost per minute (15 pence) and adding on the borrowing charge of £7.50

   a) Write a formula in numbers and letters to show this. ....

   b) Harry hired a boat for 37 minutes. How much did he have to pay?

   ....   2 marks

2. To find the area (A) of a triangle, you multiply the base (b) by the height (h) and divide the answer by 2

   a) Write a formula using numbers and letters to show this. ....

   b) Work out the area of the triangle when the base is 9 cm and the height is 12 cm.

   ....

   c) Work out the height of the triangle when the area is 10.5 cm² and the base is 7 cm.

   ....   3 marks

3. A company organises treetop climbing adventures.
   They charge £43.50 per group for an adventure.
   They also charge £7.20 per person (n) for equipment hire.

   a) Write a formula using numbers and letters to show this. ....

   b) What is the total cost of an adventure for a group of 5 friends?

   ....

   c) A group of 4 friends have a voucher that gives them 50p per person off the price of equipment hire. Write a new formula to show the cost using the voucher. Then work out the total cost for the group.

   ....

   ....   4 marks

43

Formula problems

1. For a class treasure hunt, each child provides 5 sweets and the teacher provides an extra 18

   a) Write a formula using numbers and letters to show this.
   Use *T* to represent the total number of sweets and *n* to represent the number of children.

   ....

   b) There are 37 children in the class. How many sweets are there?

   ....

   c) Jordan tells his mum that there were 19 children in his class today and they had 114 sweets for their treasure hunt in total. Is he right? How do you know?

   > Work backwards to check whether there is a whole number of children.

   ....

   ....   **4 marks**

2. Polly wants to hire a bicycle. It costs £2.00 per hour plus a fixed fee of £8.50

   > Choose a letter to represent the total cost, and another letter to represent the number of hours.

   a) Write a formula to help Polly work out the cost of hiring a bike for different numbers of hours.

   ....

   b) Polly hires a bicycle for 4.5 hours. How much does it cost?

   ....

   c) On another day, Polly hires a bicycle and pays £21.50

   How long did she hire the bicycle for?

   ....

   ....   **4 marks**

Linear sequences

1. Find the missing numbers in these linear
   sequences.

   > In a linear sequence, the numbers change by the same amount each time.

   a) 2, ..., 16, 23, ..., 37, ..., 51, 58

   b) 7, ..., 15, 19, ..., ..., ..., 35, ...   **2 marks**

2. For each of the sequences in question 1, write the term-to-term rule.
   The first part has been started for you.

   a) first term = ...2......

      add ...... to the previous term

   b) first term = ...

      add ...... to the previous term   **2 marks**

3. Find the missing numbers in these sequences.
   Then write the term-to-term rule for each.

   a) −3, ..., 7, ..., ..., 22, 27, ..., ...

      term-to-term rule: ....

   b) ......, ..., 23, ..., 16, 12.5, ..., ..., ...

      term-to-term rule: ....   **4 marks**

4. Generate the first 10 terms of these sequences.

   a) first term = 6, add 4.5 to the previous term

      ....

   b) first term = 99, subtract 13 from the previous term

      ....   **2 marks**

45

Two unknowns

1. $p = 12 - h$

   In this equation, p and h are positive integers less than 9

   List all the numbers they could be.

   > Remember that 0 is not a positive integer.

   ....

   .... **4 marks**

2. $r - s = 6$

   In this equation, r and s are positive integers less than 12

   List all the numbers they could be.

   ....

   .... **4 marks**

3. $q + 9 = r$

   In this equation, q and r are positive integers less than 20

   List all the numbers they could be.

   ....

   .... **4 marks**

4. Mariam is thinking of a pair of numbers. She tells her friend that if you add them together and subtract 3, the answer is 7

   She also says that both numbers are positive integers less than 10

   List all the numbers Mariam could be thinking of.

   ....

   .... **4 marks**

Combination problems

1. A toyshop sells wooden horses in three colours: brown, grey and black.
   For each colour of horse, there are three sizes: small, medium and large.

   a) Complete the table to show all the combinations of colour and size.

black small		
		grey large
	brown medium	

   b) Complete the calculation to show the total number of combinations.

   3 × 3 = ...   **2 marks**

2. A hat shop sells hats in 4 different colours: red, blue, green, yellow.
   For each colour there are 3 different designs: stars, stripes and plain.

   a) List all the possible combinations of colour and pattern. The first colour has been done for you.

   <u>red stars, red stripes, red plain</u>   ....

   ....

   b) Complete the calculation to show the total number of combinations.

   ...... × ...... = ...   **2 marks**

3. A shop sells card in 2 sizes: A4 and A5. Each comes in white, black, red, blue, green and cream.

   a) Draw a table below to show all the possible combinations of size and colour.

   b) Write and complete a calculation that shows the total number of combinations.

   ....   **2 marks**

Equivalent expressions

1. Read the statements below. Write whether each one is true or false.

   a) $f + g$ is the same as $g + f$ ....

   b) $y \times z$ is the same as yz ....

   c) $h \times g$ is not the same as hg ....

   d) $r \div s$ is the same as $s \div r$ ....

   e) $k - l$ is the same as $l - k$ ....

   f) $v \times w$ is the same as $w \times v$ ....

   The rules of operations still apply when numbers are used as well as letters.

   6 marks

2. Circle the expressions that are equivalent to $3d - 2e$

   $d - 2e + 2d$ $3e - 2d$ $2d + 3e$ $d + d + d - 2e$

   $3d \div 2e$ $d + d + d - e - e$ $3d - e - e$ $d + d + 2d - 2e$

   4 marks

3. Write an equivalent expression for each of the expressions below.

   a) $h + h + h + h$ ....

   b) $k \times 7$ ....

   c) $l + l - 3$ ....

   d) $m + m + m - n - n$ ....

   e) $h + h - i$ ....

   f) $y \times y$ ....

   g) $k + k + k + k - l - l - k$ ....

   h) $w + w + w + w - 2x + x$ ....

   8 marks

Algebra tips

1. Draw lines to link each calculation to the correct answer.

   $r \div 1$ $3b$

   $g \times 1$ 0

   $h \div h$ ab

   $3b \times 1$ $3s$

   $3s \div 1$ g

   $(a \times b) \times 0$ 1

   $(a \times b) \div 1$ r

   > Remember that multiplying by 0 always gives 0. If you multiply or divide by 1, the number stays the same.

   7 marks

2. The letter g represents an odd number. Circle the appropriate word to show whether the answers to these calculations will be odd or even.

   a) $g + g$ = odd / even   **b)** $g - g$ = odd / even

   c) $g + 6$ = odd / even   **d)** $12 + g$ = odd / even

   e) $g - 2$ = odd / even   **f)** $16 - g$ = odd / even

   g) $g \div 1$ = odd / even   **h)** $g \times 0$ = odd / even   **8 marks**

3. Josie thinks of an integer and adds 8 to it. She then divides the answer by itself. What number is her final answer?

   6 94 9 15 247 293 903 7 2536 83 372 284 73 1 17 94 835 953 28 42

   ....

   ....

   1 mark

4. Chad thinks of an even number and subtracts an odd number from it.
   He then multiplies the result by 1.
   Will his final answer be odd or even? Explain how you know.

   ....

   ....   **1 mark**

Units of length

1. Fill in the blanks to show the equivalent lengths using different units.

> Learn the rules for multiplying and dividing using powers of 10 to help you convert between units of measure.

   a) 10 mm   = ... cm

   b) 1 m   = ... cm

   c) 10 m   = ... cm   d) 1,000 m   = ... km

   e) 8 km   = ... m   f) 100 cm   = ... mm

6 marks

2. Convert these lengths to the units given in brackets.

   a) 3,500 m (km)   = ...   b) 9.5 km (m)   = ...

   c) 895 cm (m)   = ...   d) 7.2 m (cm)   = ...

   e) 12 cm (mm)   = ...   f) 29 mm (cm)   = ...

   g) 8,956 cm (mm)   = ...   h) 89.5 m (cm)   = ...

8 marks

3. Here are two lengths: 987 cm   9.9 m

   a) Circle the longer length.

   b) How much longer is it? ....

2 marks

4. Andrew needs 6.5 m of rope. He buys 6,850 mm of rope.
   How much spare rope does he have? Give your answer in centimetres.

....

....

....

2 marks

Weight, capacity, volume

1. Fill in the blanks to show the equivalent measurements using different units.

    a) 150 g   = ... kg   **b)** 7.5 kg   = ... g

    c) 4.5 litres   = ... ml   **d)** 678 ml   = ... litres

    e) 1 m³   = ... cm³   **f)** 67 cm³   = ... m³

6 marks

2. Convert these measurements to the units given in brackets.

    a) 567 g (kg)   = ...   **b)** 9675 cm³ (m³)   = ...

    c) 8.5 m³ (cm³)   = ...   **d)** 18567 ml (litres)   = ...

4 marks

3. Circle the larger measurement in each pair. Then write the difference between the two measurements.

    a) Which is larger?   89.7 litres   8,970 ml

       difference: ....

    b) Which is longer?   7,895 cm³   78.95 m³

       difference: ....

    c) Which is heavier?   75 kg   750,000 g

       difference: ....

6 marks

4. Jane has a swimming pool in her garden.
It has a capacity of 375 m³   1 m³ = 1,000,000 cm³

    a) What is the volume in cm³?

    ....

    b) Jane has 356,000,000 cm³ of water. How much more does she need in m³?

    ....

    ....   2 marks

51

Imperial units

1. Use this table to work out the imperial/metric conversions for the following measurements:

> Imperial and metric conversions are not exact. The ≈ sign shows this.

length	weight	capacity
1 mile ≈ 1.6 km	1 pound ≈ 400 g	1 pint ≈ 500 ml
1 inch ≈ 2.5 cm	1 ounce ≈ 30 g	

a) 7 miles   ≈ .... km

b) 75 g   ≈ .... ounces

c) 12 pints   ≈ .... ml

d) 1,000 g   ≈ .... pounds

e) 12.5 cm   ≈ .... inches

f) 7 inches   ≈ .... cm

g) 12.5 pounds ≈ .... g   **7 marks**

2. Grace is going to make a cake. Her recipe uses imperial measures. Convert them to metric. Write your answers in the table.

> Write down your working to make it easier to check later.

Grace's recipe	metric measures
$\frac{3}{4}$ pound flour	
$\frac{1}{2}$ pound sugar	
5 ounces butter	
1 ounce salt	
$\frac{1}{4}$ pint of milk	

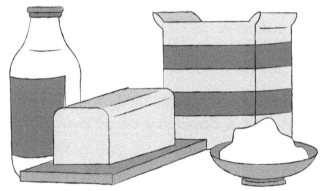

5 marks

Time problems

1. Fill in the blanks to show the equivalent times using different units.

    a) 210 seconds   = ... minutes

    b) 75 years   = ... decades

    c) 312 weeks   = ... years

    d) 14.5 days   = ... hours

    e) 54 months   = ... years

    f) 7 hours   = ... minutes   **6 marks**

2. Fill in the blanks to convert each of these times into three different units.

    a) 5.5 days   = ... hours   = ... minutes = ... seconds

    b) 4 centuries = ... decades = ... years   = ... months

                                                                        6 marks

3. Emily looks at her digital watch. The time is 11:45

    a) Draw this time on the analogue clock.

    b) Emily looks at her watch again
        2 hours and 21 minutes later.
        Write this time on the digital clock.

                                                                      2 marks

4. Chloe announces she is 2,558 days old.   Assume each year
                                                       is 365 days long.

    a) How old is Chloe in years and days?

    ....

    b) How old is Chloe in weeks and days?

    ....

    c) How many minutes old is Chloe?

    ....   **3 marks**

Measurement calculations

1. Find the sums of the following measurements.
   Use the space below to write out your working.

   a) 7.6 litres + 567 ml   **b)** 75,609 g + 4.5 kg

   > Make sure the measurements are all in the same units before doing your calculations.

   ....

   4 marks

2. Shauna is measuring how much fabric she needs for some dresses she is making. She needs 2.5 m of one fabric, 167 cm of another, 3.4 m of another and 560 mm of another.

   a) Write all the measurements in centimetres.

   ....

   ....

   b) In total, how much material does she need in metres?

   ....

   ....   **4 marks**

3. Travellers are allowed 22.5 kg of hold luggage when flying on an aeroplane. Nadim's case weighs 22,967 g.

   a) How much extra does he have in grams?

   ....

   ....

   b) The airline charges £15 for each extra 100 g or part of 100 g. How much does Nadim have to pay?

   ....

   ....   **4 marks**

Perimeter and area

1. Work out the missing measurements for these rectangles.

    a) A rectangle with sides of length 12 cm and 5 cm.

    > The formula for the perimeter of a rectangle is
    > $P = 2 \times (l + w)$

    perimeter = ... area = ...

    b) A rectangle with length 15 cm and perimeter 42 cm.

    width = ... area = ...

    c) A rectangle with area 137.5 cm² and length 22 cm.

    width = ... perimeter = ...

    6 marks

2. Rectangle F has a width of 9 cm and an area of 135 cm².
   Rectangle G has the same perimeter as F and a length of 11 cm.
   What is the area of rectangle G?

   > Draw a sketch to help you.

   .... **3 marks**

Compound shapes

1. Find the perimeter and area of this shape.

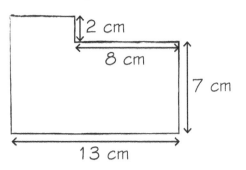

> To find the perimeter of a compound shape, find the unknown lengths and add all the sides together.

perimeter = ...

area   = ...

2 marks

2. Find the perimeter and area of this shape.

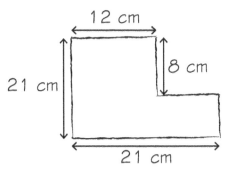

> To find the area of a compound shape, split the shape into rectangles and find the area of each one.

perimeter = ...

area   = ...

2 marks

3. Katya cuts four identical squares out of the corners of a square of fabric to make a cross. Find the perimeter and area of the cross.

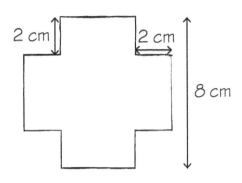

perimeter = ...

area   = ...

2 marks

56

Parallelograms

1. Work out the area of a parallelogram with base length 17 cm and perpendicular height 9 cm.

> Area of parallelogram (A) = length of base (b) × perpendicular height (h) or $A = b \times h$

....

....

3 marks

2. Find the perimeter and area of each of these parallelograms.

a)

9 cm   56 cm $h = 7$ cm

> Remember to include the correct units in your answer.

perimeter = ...   area = ...

b)

7 cm   33 cm $h = 4.5$ cm

perimeter = ...   area = ...

4 marks

Triangles

1. A triangle has base length 13 cm
   and perpendicular height 9 cm.
   Work out its area.

> Area of triangle (A) = $\frac{1}{2}$ (length of base × perpendicular height) or A = $\frac{1}{2}$ (l × h)

....

....

                 1 mark

2. Find the perimeter and area of each of these triangles.

   a)

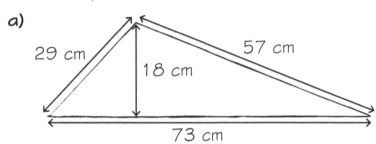

   perimeter = ...

   area   = ...

   b)

   > When a triangle has a right-angle, the perpendicular height is the same as the length of the side perpendicular to the base.

   8 cm   25 cm

   26 cm

   perimeter = ...

   area   = ...   **4 marks**

3. A triangle has an area of 54 cm² and a
   perpendicular height of 12 cm.
   Work out the length of its base.

   > Use inverse operations to help you find the base length.

....

.... **1 mark**

Volumes of cuboids

1. Find the volume of each of these cuboids.

a)

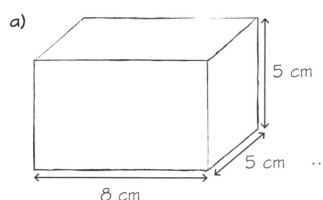

5 cm

5 cm

8 cm

....

....

b)

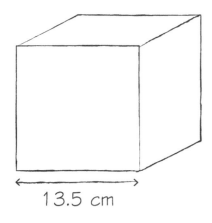

12.5 cm

3.5 cm

6.5 cm

....

....

2 marks

2. Find the volume of this cube.

13.5 cm

....

....

1 mark

3. A cube has sides with length 7 cm. A cuboid has length 0.06 m, width 4 mm and height 7 cm. What is the difference between the volumes of the two shapes?

Change all lengths to the same units and work out both volumes.

....

....

....   **3 marks**

59

Measurement problems

1. Find the area of the shaded region of these walls.

a)

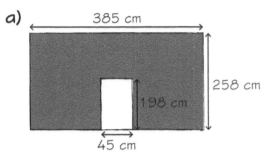

385 cm

258 cm

198 cm

45 cm

....

.... **2 marks**

b) This wall has 3 square windows. Each window has side length 70 cm.

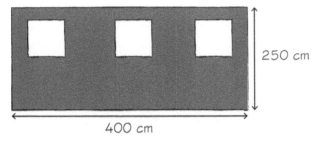

250 cm

400 cm

....

.... **2 marks**

2. A jug holds 150 cm³ of water. A bucket holds enough water to fill the jug 4.5 times. What is the capacity of the bucket?

....

.... **1 mark**

3. A 4-year-old weighs 15 kg. A 2-year-old weighs 3,000 g less than the 4-year-old. A 15-year-old weighs 40 kg more than the 2-year-old. What is the difference between the 15-year-old's weight and the 4-year-old's weight?

> Find out what the 2-year-old weighs. Then work out how much the 15-year-old weighs.

....

.... **3 marks**

2D shapes

1. Name these triangles.

a)

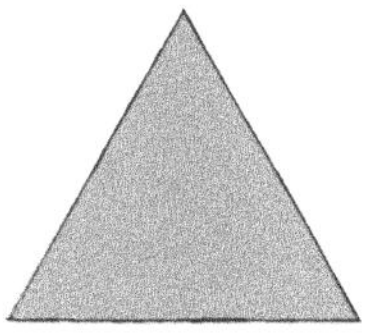

....

b)

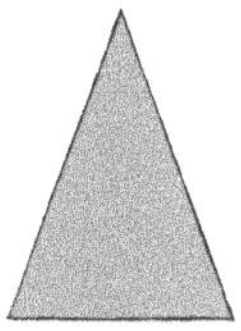

....

c)

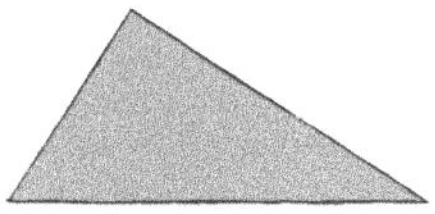

....

d)

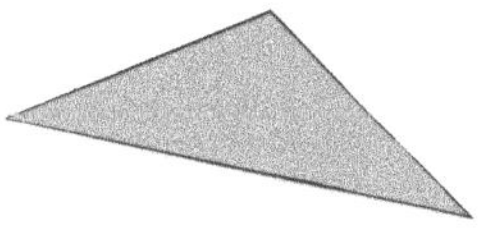

.... 4 marks

2. Write the name of each polygon and circle whether it is regular or irregular.

a) 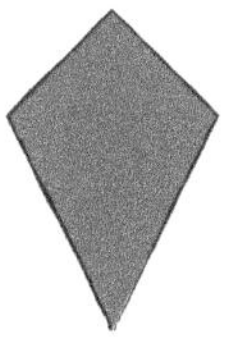 .... regular / irregular

b) 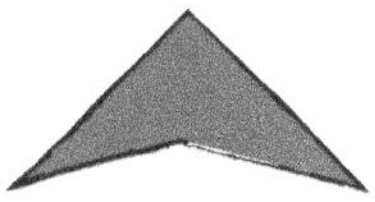 .... regular / irregular

c) .... regular / irregular

6 marks

3. A shape has 4 sides of equal length and two different pairs of equal opposite angles. What shape is it?

.... 1 mark

4. I am a regular polygon. I have 8 sides of equal length and 8 equal angles. What am I?

.... 1 mark

Angles

1. Write whether each angle that is marked is obtuse, acute or reflex.

a)

b)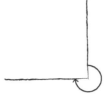

c)

d)

....

4 marks

2. Write in the unknown angles on each of these diagrams.

a)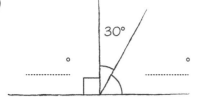

b)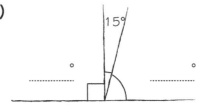

2 marks

3. Write in the unknown angles on these diagrams.

a)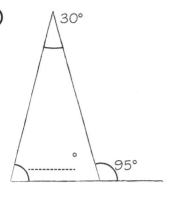

b)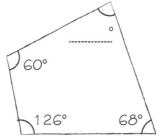

c)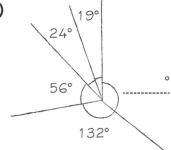

3 marks

Angle problems

1. Find the size of each unknown angle in these diagrams.

a)

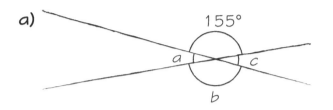

155°

a = ...°

b = ...°

c = ...°

b)

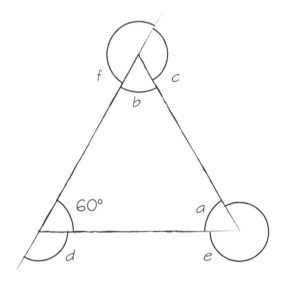

105°

a = ...°

b = ...°

c = ...°

6 marks

2. Work out the size of each angle in this diagram. The triangle is equilateral.

60°

a = ...°

b = ...°

c = ...°

d = ...°

e = ...°

f = ...°

6 marks

Circles

1. Work out the radius or diameter of each of these circles.

a)

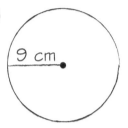

9 cm

b)

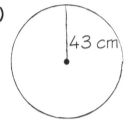

43 cm

c)

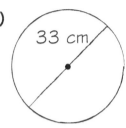

33 cm

diameter = ...   diameter = ...   radius = ...

3 marks

2. Each of these circles is cut in half. Write the areas of the semi-circles that are created.

a)

area = 0.88 m²

b)

area = 144.4 cm²

....   2 marks

3. Write down which feature has been marked on each of these circles.

a)

b)

c)

....   3 marks

4. Four identical small circles fit inside a large circle.

The centre of the large circle is in the same place as the centre of one of the small circles.

The diameter of a small circle is 15 cm.
What is the radius of the large circle?

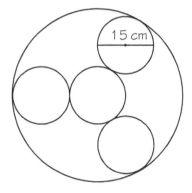

15 cm

....

....

3D shapes

1. Read each description. What is the 3D shape?

   a) This shape has 9 edges, 5 faces and 6 vertices.
   Its faces are 3 rectangles and 2 isosceles triangles.

   ....

   b) This shape has 1 face.

   ....

   c) This shape has 2 edges, 3 faces and 0 vertices.
   Its faces are 1 rectangle and 2 circles.

   ....

   d) This shape has 1 edge, 2 faces and 1 vertex.
   Its faces are 1 circle and 1 semi-circle.

   .... **4 marks**

2. Complete the table.

name of shape	number of faces	number of vertices	number of edges
cube			12
cuboid		8	
tetrahedron			
octahedron		6	12
triangular prism		6	

5 marks

number of faces +
number of vertices =
number of edges + 2

Nets

1. Circle the diagram that is not the net of a cube.

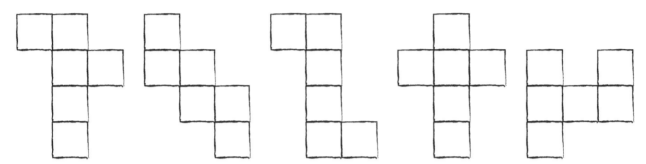

1 mark

2. Write the names of the shapes these nets make.

Imagine folding the nets to make a 3D shape.

a)

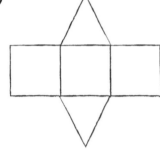

b)

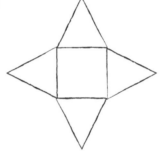

c)

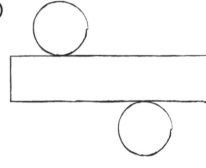

....

3 marks

3. Sketch the net of a hexagonal-based prism.

2 marks

Coordinates

1. Write the coordinates for each of the crosses marked on the graph below.

   A (........., ...)

   B (........., ...)

   C (........., ...)

   D (........., ...)

   E (........., ...)

   F (........., ...)

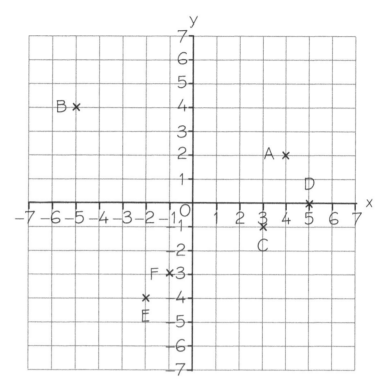

   6 marks

2. These coordinates are all on a straight line. Is the line horizontal or vertical? Explain how you know.

   (−3, 56)   (−3, −19)   (−3, 0)   (−3, 2)

   ....

   .... 2 marks

3. On the graph above, draw a diagonal line that passes through the points (−4, −2) and (1, 3). Write down the coordinates of three other points on the line.

   (........., ...)   (........., ...)   (........., ...)   4 marks

Translations

1. Here are two shapes on a coordinate grid.

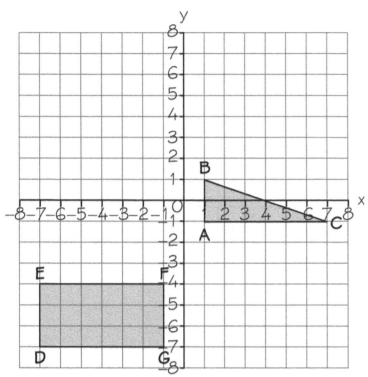

a) Write the coordinates of the labelled vertices.

A (...1.., ...–1..)

B (......, ...)

C (......, ...)

D (..–7.., ..–7..)

E (......, ...)

F (......, ...)

G (......, ...)   2 marks

b) Translate each shape 5 squares up and 1 to the right. Write the new coordinates of the vertices.

triangle: A (...2.., ...4..)   B (......, ...)   C (......, ...)

rectangle: D (......, ...)   E (......, ...)   F (......, ...)   G (......, ...)

4 marks

2. A triangle has vertices at (–2, –3), (–2, 1) and (3, 2).

a) Chloe translates the triangle 2 places to the left.
Give the new coordinates of the vertices of the triangle.

(........., ...)   (........., ...,)   (........., ...)

b) Deepak translates the original triangle 4 places up.
Give the new coordinates of the vertices of the triangle.

(........., ...)   (........., ...,)   (........., ...)

c) Kim translates the triangle so that the vertex at (3, 2) is now at (1, –2).
Write the coordinates of the other two vertices.

(........., ...)   (........., ...,)

3 marks

Reflection

1. Here is a square on a coordinate grid. The square has an area of 16 units.

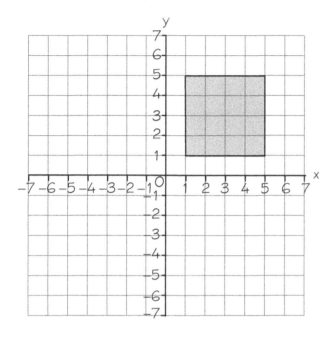

a) Draw three reflections of the square so that it appears in the other three quadrants.

b) In a different colour, draw a rectangle with an area of 16 units. Draw three reflections of it so that it appears in the other three quadrants.

2 marks

2. The vertices of square A are at (−3, 3) (−1, 3) (−1, 1) and (−3, 1).

a) Karen reflects square A in the x-axis.
   What are the new coordinates of the square?

   (......., ...,)   (......., ...)   (......., ...)   (......., ...)

> When you reflect a shape in the x-axis, only the y-coordinate changes.

b) Habib reflects square A in the y-axis.
   What are the new coordinates of the square?

   (......., ...,)   (......., ...)   (......., ...)   (......., ...)

2 marks

3. The vertices of rectangle B are at (1, −2), (1, −4), (10, −4) and (10, −2).

a) Jack reflects rectangle B in the x-axis.
   What are the new coordinates of the rectangle?

   (......., ...,)   (......., ...)   (......., ...)   (......., ...)

b) Indira reflects rectangle B in the y-axis.
   What are the new coordinates of the rectangle?

   (......., ...,)   (......., ...)   (......., ...)   (......., ...)

2 marks

Tables

1. Here is part of a local school football league table. Use the table to answer the questions below.

position	team	played	won	drawn	lost	goals scored	goals conceded	goal difference	points
1	Whalley Grammar	35	25	5	5	96	44	52	80
2	Ribble High	35	23	6	6	67	26	41	75
3	Ivy Row	34	23	5	6	91	35	56	74
4	St Cecelia's	35	21	7	7	62	41	21	70
5	Chatburn Road	35	20	9	6	57	34	23	69
6	Queen Elizabeth's	35	19	6	10	51	49	2	63
7	Moor Lock Academy	34	17	6	11	56	40	16	57
8	St Mark's	35	13	10	12	50	45	5	49

a) Which team is in 5th position?

....   **1 mark**

b) How many games have Moor Lock Academy lost?

....   **1 mark**

c) One team has scored 67 goals. How many points does that team have?

....   **1 mark**

d) Which team has drawn the most games?

....   **1 mark**

e) Which team has 12 more points than Queen Elizabeth's?

....   **1 mark**

f) How many more games have St Cecelia's won than lost?

....   **2 marks**

Bar charts

1. Mr O'Reilly asked the children in Year 6 what their favourite pet is. He recorded the results in this graph.

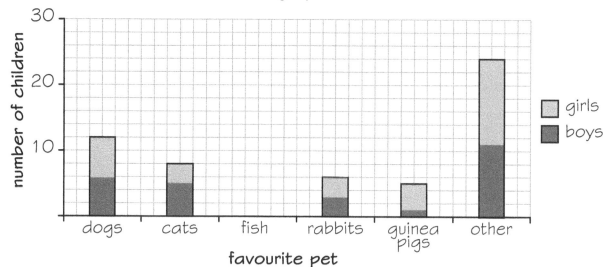

a) Mr O'Reilly has forgotten to draw one of the bars. Eleven boys and seven girls like fish best. Complete the bar chart.

> Look at the key. Make sure you shade the bar correctly.

1 mark

b) How many children did not choose fish or 'other'?

.... 1 mark

c) Which animals were chosen by the same number of girls as boys?

.... 1 mark

d) What is the difference between the number of children who chose the three least popular choices and the number who chose the three most popular choices?

.... 1 mark

e) How many boys are in Year 6?

.... 1 mark

f) What percentage of girls liked dogs or rabbits best?

....

.... 2 marks

71

Reading pie charts

1. This pie chart shows how 48 children at Sallyforth school travelled to school one day. Use the pie chart to answer the questions.

   a) How many children travelled to school by car?

   ....

   b) How many children travelled to school by bike?

   ....

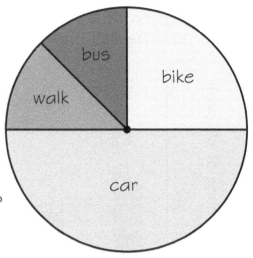

2 marks

2. This pie chart shows how 24 children at Victoria school got to school on the same day. Use the pie chart to answer the questions.

   a) How many children travelled to school by car?

   ....

   b) How many children travelled to school by bike or bus?

   ....

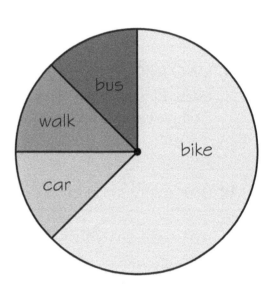

   ....

2 marks

3. Compare both pie charts. How many more children travelled by bike at Victoria school than at Sallyforth School?

> Remember that the pie charts represent different numbers of children.

....

.... 1 mark

Pie chart problems

1. Together, these pie charts show 96 children's favourite genres of film.

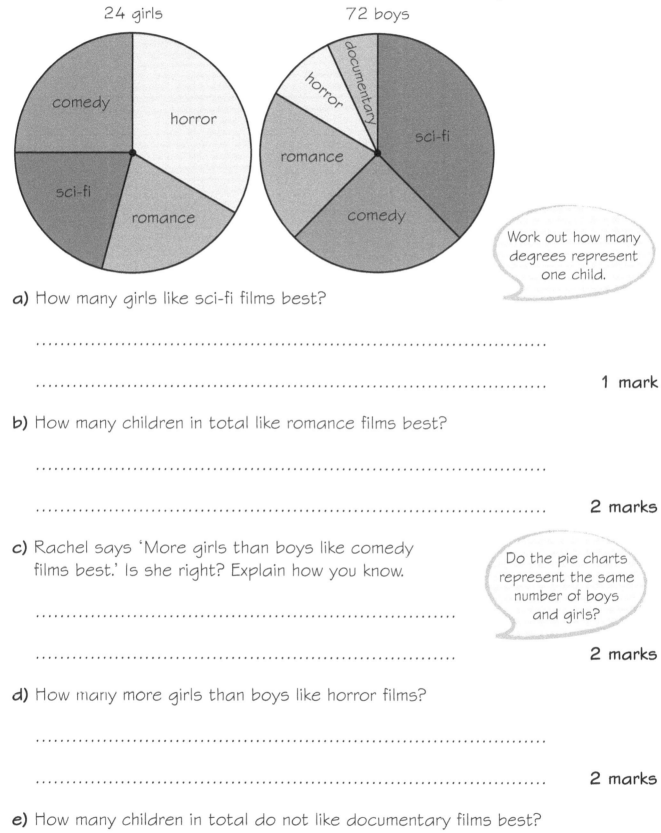

24 girls   72 boys

Work out how many degrees represent one child.

a) How many girls like sci-fi films best?

....

....   1 mark

b) How many children in total like romance films best?

....

....   2 marks

c) Rachel says 'More girls than boys like comedy films best.' Is she right? Explain how you know.

Do the pie charts represent the same number of boys and girls?

....

....   2 marks

d) How many more girls than boys like horror films?

....

....   2 marks

e) How many children in total do not like documentary films best?

....

....   2 marks

73

Drawing pie charts

1. Freya asks the children in her class to choose their favourite ice cream flavour from a short list. The table shows some of her results.

favourite flavour of ice cream	number of children	angle of the slice
strawberry	8	
vanilla	3	
chocolate	15	180°
mint		48°

3 marks

a) Complete the table.

b) How many children in total are in the class?

....   **1 mark**

c) Using the circle below, draw a pie chart to show the children's choices of ice cream flavour.

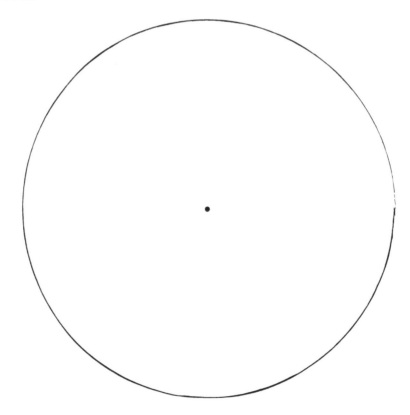

4 marks

Line graphs

1. Shelley wears an exercise tracker to measure how far she walks one day on the Malvern Hills. She checks it throughout the day and records the results on this graph. Use the graph to answer the questions.

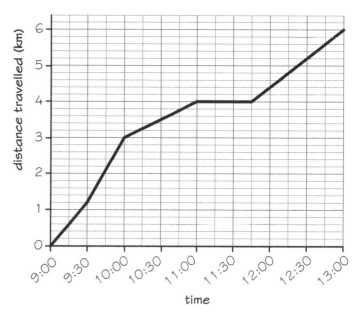

a) At what time did Shelley turn on the exercise tracker?

....

....

b) At what time did Shelley turn off the tracker?

....

c) How many metres did Shelley walk during the day?

....

d) By what time had Shelley walked 1.2 km?

....

> Go up the vertical axis until you reach 1.2 km, then read across to the line.

e) How far had Shelley walked by 12:00?

....

f) Between which two times did Shelley stop for a break?

....

g) How far did Shelley walk between 12:00 and 13:00?

....

h) Between which two times is Shelley walking most quickly?

....   **8 marks**

Mean

1. Find the mean of the values in each set.

   a) 3, 3, 4, 4, 5, 5, 6, 6

   ....

   > To find the mean, add up all of the numbers and divide by how many numbers there are.

   b) 3, 4, 5, 6, 7, 8, 9, 10

   ....

   c) 12, 34, 6, 19, 43, 6

   .... **3 marks**

2. Erica saves a mean of £3.60 each day in March. For the first 10 days in March, she saves £2.95 per day. For the next 10 days, she saves £4.20 per day. For the next 10 days, she saves £3.70 per day. How much does she save on the last day of March?

   ....

   .... **1 mark**

3.

   | 7 | 6 | 9 | 10 | | 12 | 3 | 5 | 11 | 21 |

   Find the missing number on these ten cards if the mean of the numbers is:

   a) 10.1   ....

   b) 9.9   ....

   c) 10.5   .... **3 marks**

Answers

NUMBER

1 Place value

1. a) 900
   b) 90,000
   c) 900,000
   d) 90
   e) 90,000
   f) 9,000,000
   g) 9,000
2. b) ten thousands
   c) hundred thousands
   d) thousands
   e) hundreds
3. a) 20,000
   b) 100
   c) 300,000
   d) 2,000,000
   e) 1,000
4. b) 6,300,000
   c) 4,995,000
   d) 999,990

2 Number lines

1. a) 5   b) 0.01   c) 0.02   d) 0.1
2. a) 120,000   120,500

   b) 120,000   130,000

3. B

3 Negative numbers

1. b) 14 degrees   c) 6.5 degrees
2. a) 9 degrees   b) −0.7 degrees
3. 10.5 degrees   4. 40.3

4 Number line problems

1.

point in mission	depth of submarine
A	−75 m
B	−30 m
C	−120 m
D	−10 m
E	−200 m
F	−165 m
G	−90 m
H	−105 m

2. a) 135 m   b) 45 m   c) 30 m

5 Rounding

1. b) 6,723,900
   c) 6,724,000
   d) 6,720,000
   e) 6,700,000
   f) 7,000,000
2. b) Any number between 10,865 and 10,874
   c) Any number between 432,395 and 432,404
   d) Any number between 1,067,075 and 1,067,084
3. b) Any number between 102,500 and 103,499
   c) Any number between 979,500 and 980,499
   d) Any number between 909,500 and 910,499
4. £53.00

6 Rounding problems

1. a) 2,425   b) 22,500   c) 4,500,00
2. a) 1,349   b) 264,999   c) 849,999
3. b) smallest: 344,500 largest: 345,499
   c) smallest: 2,339,500 largest: 2,340,499
4. a) 77,500 and 78,499
   b) 550,000 and 649,999

7 Roman numerals

1.

Roman numeral	I	V	X	L	C	D	M
value of Roman numeral	1	5	10	50	100	500	1,000

2. a) 3   b) 55   c) 550   d) 1,498
3. a) LXXXIV   b) CCXLVII   c) DCCCLIV   d) MMMXII
4. a) 620   b) 3,699   c) 2,900
5. 3,458 miles

CALCULATION

8 Addition

1. a) 897,931   b) 157.5   c) 765,780
2. a) 1,859,853   b) 5,102,006
   c) 944.804   d) 2,208.14

9 Subtraction

1. a) 217,332   b) 63,920   c) 436.9
2. a) 6,332,935   b) 1,846,112
   c) 307.94   d) 82.597

10 Add/subtract problems

1. 29,250 miles
2. £11.49
3. 298.9 ml

11 Multiples

1. multiples of 3: 3, 6, 9, 12, 15, 18, 21, 24, 27, 30
   multiples of 6: 6, 12, 18, 24, 30
   multiples of 10: 10, 20, 30
2. 6, 12, 18, 24, 30
3. Yes, because 9 is a multiple of 45 so 90 must be a multiple of 4,500
4. These numbers should be circled:
   56   112   217   392   1,400
5. No. 29,173 divided by 16 does not give a whole number so 29,173 is not a multiple of 16

12 Factors

1. a) 1, 2, 3, 6, 9, 18
   b) 1, 2, 17, 34
   c) 1, 2, 4, 8, 16, 32, 64
   d) 1, 2, 3, 6, 13, 26, 39, 78
2. 1, 3, 9
3. 20

Answers

13 Prime numbers

1. 2, 3, 5, 7, 11, 13, 17, 19, 23, 29, 31, 37, 41, 43, 47
2. b) $2 \times 3 \times 5$ c) 2×17
   d) 2×23 e) 7×7
   f) $2 \times 3 \times 13$
3. 61, 97, 101, 103, 139, 163, 199
4. Yes. Your working should show that 307 can only be divided by itself and 1
5. $7 \times 5 \times 2$

14 Squares and cubes

1. b) $7 \times 7 = 49$ c) $9 \times 9 = 81$
2. a) 64   b) 121   c) 225
3. b) $4 \times 4 \times 4 = 64$ c) $5 \times 5 \times 5 = 125$
4. a) 64   216   343   216,000
   b) 4^3 6^3 7^3 60^3

15 Moving digits

1. b)

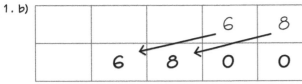

c)

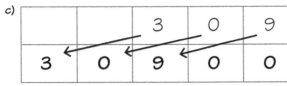

d)

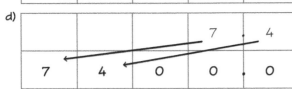

2. a) 645.7   6.457
   b) 1185.6   11.856
   c) 65.473   0.65473
3. £75.00   4. £24.70

16 Multiplication

1. b) 2,832   c) 16,923
2. b) 64,200   c) 58,938
3. 13,860 ml

17 Division

1. b) 879.375   c) 2250.75
2. b) Multiples of 48 = 48, 96, 144, 192, 240, 288, 336
   167 r 16
3. 102

18 Remainders

1. 5 packs   2. 15 packs   3. a) £56.34   b) 7p

19 Multi-step problems

1. a) £5.29   b) £63.48
2. £40.40   3. 404 points

20 Order of operations

1. a) 33   b) 8   c) 52
   d) 19   e) 97   f) 32

2. a) 18   32.66   difference = 14.66
   b) 26   10   difference = 16
3. a) $(7 + 3) \times 5 \div (1 + 4) = 10$
   b) $(10 + 30) \div (15 + 5) = 2$
   c) $(12 + 9) \div 3 + 3 = 10$
4. $54 + (84.76 - 20) \div 2 = £86.38$

21 Solving problems

1. a) 117   b) 225
2. a) 52×14 b) 83×23

FRACTIONS, DECIMALS AND PERCENTAGES

22 Equivalent fractions

1. a) 16   b) 15   c) 66   d) 2   e) 8   f) 35
2. $\frac{5}{7} = \frac{45}{63}$ $\frac{1}{4} = \frac{40}{160}$ $\frac{2}{3} = \frac{44}{66}$ $\frac{8}{13} = \frac{16}{26}$ $\frac{3}{8} = \frac{27}{72}$
3. $\frac{35}{40}$ $\frac{63}{72}$
4. Any five of the following:
   $\frac{3}{4}$ $\frac{6}{8}$ $\frac{24}{32}$ $\frac{36}{48}$ $\frac{48}{64}$ $\frac{60}{80}$ $\frac{72}{96}$
   or other equivalent fractions that are correct.

23 Simplest form

1. a) $\frac{4}{5}$ b) $\frac{3}{5}$ c) $\frac{13}{18}$ d) $\frac{9}{13}$ e) $\frac{7}{11}$
2. b) $\frac{3}{7}$ c) $\frac{13}{32}$ d) $\frac{15}{299}$ e) $\frac{3}{4}$ f) $\frac{13}{18}$

24 Ordering fractions

1. b) $4\frac{1}{4}$ c) $2\frac{11}{12}$ d) $14\frac{2}{5}$
2. b) $\frac{42}{11}$ c) $\frac{47}{17}$ d) $\frac{61}{7}$
3. a) $\frac{9}{12}$ $\frac{23}{4}$ $9\frac{3}{4}$
   b) $\frac{30}{6}$ $5\frac{3}{12}$ $\frac{17}{3}$

25 Add/subtract fractions

1. a) $\frac{7}{12} + \frac{8}{12} + \frac{10}{12} = 2\frac{1}{12}$
   b) $\frac{6}{9} + \frac{15}{9} + \frac{2}{9} = 2\frac{5}{9}$
   c) $\frac{120}{30} + \frac{18}{30} + \frac{21}{30} = 5\frac{3}{10}$
2. a) $\frac{5}{3}$ b) $\frac{4}{5}$ c) $\frac{29}{3}$

26 Multiplying fractions

1. a) $1\frac{5}{7}$ b) $2\frac{6}{7}$ c) $4\frac{4}{7}$ d) $5\frac{1}{7}$ e) $7\frac{3}{7}$
2. $3\frac{3}{4}$
3. a) $\frac{4}{7}$ b) $4\frac{1}{8}$ c) $\frac{8}{21}$ d) 1

27 Dividing fractions

1. a) $\frac{1}{40}$ b) $\frac{1}{5}$ c) $\frac{8}{63}$
2. $\frac{1}{6}$ 3. $\frac{1}{4}$
4. a) $\frac{1}{12}$ b) $\frac{1}{15}$ c) $\frac{2}{45}$

28 Decimals

1. b) 4 units   c) 1 thousandth   d) 3 tens
2. a) 0.5   b) 0.09   c) 0.007
   d) 0.64   e) 0.568   f) 0.403
3. b) $\frac{70}{100} = 0.7$ c) $\frac{34}{100} = 0.34$
   d) $\frac{770}{1000} = 0.77$ e) $\frac{72}{100} = 0.72$

29 Fractions and decimals
1. b) 0.4375   c) 0.375   d) 0.5625
2. a) 0.556   b) 0.333   c) 0.667
3. a) $\frac{1}{4}$ b) 0.25

30 Rounding decimals
1. a) 5   b) 7   c) 10   d) 21
2. a) 7.9   b) 12.7   c) 134.6   d) 22.6
3. a) 23.99   b) 88.89   c) 70.01   d) 112.11
4. b) 101.35 and 101.44   c) 0.85 and 0.94

31 Multiplying decimals
1. b) 0.03 × 7

   Multiply the decimal by 100 to get 3   3 × 7 = 21

   Divide the answer by 100 to get 0.21   0.03 × 7 = 0.21

   c) 2.4 × 9

   Multiply the decimal by 10 to get 24   24 × 9 = 216

   Divide the answer by 10 to get 21.6   2.4 × 9 = 21.6
2. £10.08
3. 1.62 km

32 Percentages
1. a) 43 out of 50 squares shaded
   b) 47 out of 100 squares shaded
   c) 3 out of 10 squares shaded
   d) 3 out of 4 squares shaded
2. 40%
3. 7.5%

33 Percentages and decimals
1. a) 65%   b) 60%
   c) 7%   d) 8.5%
2. a) 0.87   b) 0.48
   c) 0.3   d) 0.29
3. a) 30%   b) 0.25
   c) 0.45
4. a) 0.4   b) 30%
   c) 0.15   d) 15% and 0.15

34 Equivalence
1. Multiply by 100 to get 73%.
2. Find an equivalent fraction with a denominator of 100 and then read the numerator to get 80%.
3. Write the percentage as the numerator and 100 as the denominator and then simplify where possible to get $\frac{47}{50}$
4. a) 0.67, $\frac{67}{100}$ b) 0.79, $\frac{79}{100}$

   c) 0.08, $\frac{2}{25}$ d) 0.15, $\frac{3}{20}$
5. a) 7% $\frac{7}{100}$ b) 16% $\frac{4}{25}$

   c) 10% $\frac{1}{10}$ d) 40% $\frac{2}{5}$

35 Fraction problems
1. 36.67 cm
2. 177.78 m
3. 566.67 g
4. $\frac{1}{3}$

36 Finding percentages
1. 240
2. £621
3. £67.65
4. 1320 m
5. 618.8 g

RATIO AND PROPORTION
37 Ratio and proportion
1. a) $\frac{2}{10}$, 0.2, 20%   b) $\frac{2}{6}$, 0.33, 33%   c) $\frac{7}{9}$, 0.78, 78%
2. a) 1 : 4   b) 1 : 2   c) 7 : 2
3. a) 2 : 3   b) 1 : 5   c) 1 : 2   d) 3 : 1
4. 3 equivalent ratios to 6 : 2, e.g. 3 : 1, 12 : 4, 18 : 6, 24 : 8…

38 Unequal sharing
1. 330 children
2. a) 1 : 6   b) £21
3. a) 262.5 g   b) 612.5 g

39 Ratio problems
1. 40
2. 270 ml
3. 54 round biscuits
4. a) 405 ml of milk   b) 495 ml

40 Scaling
1. a) length = 125 m   height = 320 m
   b) length = 286 m   height = 18 m
2.

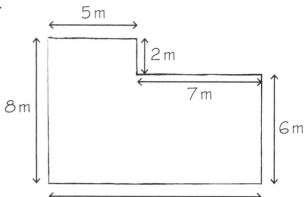

41 Similarity
1. A trapezium drawn with dimensions in proportion to the ones provided.
2. a) 1.3 cm   b) 11.7 cm
3. 12.5 cm, 22.5 cm, 35 cm

ALGEBRA
42 Using letters
1. a) 11   b) 9   c) 11.5   d) 10.5
2. a) 12   b) 3   c) 6   d) 13
3. a) 192   b) 16   c) 24   d) 55
4. −1   5. £25.92

43 Simple formulae
1. a) e.g. C = (m × 0.15) + £7.50   b) £13.05
2. a) A = (b × h) ÷ 2   b) 54 cm²   c) 3 cm

Answers

3. a) e.g. C = £43.50 + (£7.20 × n)
b) £79.50   **c)** £108.30
d) e.g. C = £43.50 + (£6.70 × 4)
    total cost is £70.30

44 Formula problems

1. a) e.g. T = 5n + 18   **b)** 203
    c) No, there would have been 113 sweets.

2. a) e.g. T = (n × £2.00) + £8.50   **b)** £17.50
    c) $6\frac{1}{2}$ hours

45 Linear sequences

1. a) 9, 30, 44   **b)** 11, 23, 27, 31, 39

2. a) first term = 2, add 7 to the previous term
    b) first term = 7, add 4 to the previous term

3. a) 2, 12, 17, 32, 37
    first term = −3, add 5 to the previous term
    b) 30, 26.5, 19.5, 9, 5.5, 2
    first term = 30, subtract 3.5 from the previous term

4. a) 6, 10.5, 15, 19.5, 24, 28.5, 33, 37.5, 42, 46.5
    b) 99, 86, 73, 60, 47, 34, 21, 8, −5, −18

46 Two unknowns

1. p = 4 h = 8,
    p = 5 h = 7,
    p = 6 h = 6,
    p = 7 h = 5,
    p = 8 h = 4

2. r = 11 s = 5,
    r = 10 s = 4,
    r = 9 s = 3,
    r = 8 s = 2,
    r = 7 s = 1

3. q = 10 r = 19, q = 9 r = 18, q = 8 r = 17, q = 7
    r = 16, q = 6 r = 15, q = 5 r = 14, q = 4 r = 13,
    q = 3 r = 12, q = 2 r = 11, q = 1 r = 10

4. 1 and 9, 2 and 8, 3 and 7, 4 and 6, 5 and 5

47 Combination problems

1. a)

black small	black medium	black large
grey small	grey medium	grey large
brown small	brown medium	brown large

    b) 3 × 3 = 9

2. a) green stars, green stripes, green plain
    blue stars, blue stripes, blue plain
    yellow stars, yellow stripes, yellow plain
    b) 3 × 4 = 12

3. a)

A4 white	A5 white
A4 black	A5 black
A4 red	A5 red
A4 blue	A5 blue
A4 green	A5 green
A4 cream	A5 cream

    b) 2 × 6 = 12

48 Equivalent expressions

1. a) true   **b)** true
    c) false   **d)** false
    e) false   **f)** true

2. d − 2e + 2d
    d + d + d − 2e
    d + d + d − e − e
    3d − e − e

3. a) 4h   **b)** 7k
    c) 2l − 3   **d)** 3m − 2n
    e) 2h − i   **f)** y^2
    g) 3k − 2l   **h)** 4w − x

49 Algebra tips

1. r ÷ 1 = r
    g × 1 = g
    h ÷ h = 1
    3b × 1 = 3b
    3s ÷ 1 = 3s
    (a × b) × 0 = 0
    (a × b) ÷ 1 = ab

2. a) even   **b)** even   **c)** odd   **d)** odd
    e) odd   **f)** odd   **g)** odd   **h)** even

3. 1 (odd)

4. even − odd = odd
    odd × 1 = odd
    so his final answer will be odd.

MEASUREMENT

50 Units of length

1. a) 11 cm   **b)** 100 cm
    c) 1,000 cm   **d)** 1 km
    e) 8,000 m   **f)** 1,000 mm

2. a) 3.50 km   **b)** 9,500 m
    c) 8.950 m   **d)** 720 cm
    e) 120 mm   **f)** 2.90 cm
    g) 89,560 mm   **h)** 8,950 cm

3. a) 9.9 m circled   **b)** 3 cm

4. 35 cm

51 Weight, capacity, volume

1. a) 0.150 kg   **b)** 7,500 g
    c) 4,500 ml   **d)** 0.678 litres
    e) 1,000,000 cm³   **f)** 0.000067 m³

2. a) 0.567 kg   **b)** 0.009675 m³
    c) 8,500,000 cm³   **d)** 18.567 litres

3. a) circled = 89.70 litres, difference = 80,730 ml
    b) circled = 78.95 m³, difference = 78,942,105 cm³
    c) circled = 750,000 g, difference = 675,000 g

4. a) 375,000,000 cm³   **b)** 19 m³

52 Imperial units

1. a) 11.2 km   **b)** 2.5 ounces   **c)** 6,000 ml
    d) 2.5 pounds   **e)** 5 inches   **f)** 17.5 cm
    g) 5,000 g

2. 300 g flour, 200 g sugar, 150 g butter, 30 g salt, 125 ml milk

53 Time problems

1. a) 3.5 minutes   **b)** 7.5 decades
    c) 6 years   **d)** 348 hours
    e) 4.5 years   **f)** 420 minutes

2. a) 132 hours, 7,920 minutes, 475,200 seconds
    b) 40 decades, 400 years, 4,800 months

3. a) The big hand should point to the 9. The small hand should be $\frac{3}{4}$ of the way between 11 and 12.

  b) 14:06

4. a) 7 years 3 days old   **b)** 365 weeks and 3 days

  c) 3,683,520 minutes

54 Measurement calculations

1. a) 8,167 ml (8.167 l)   **b)** 80,109 g (80.109 kg)

2. a) 250 cm, 340 cm, 56 cm   **b)** 8.13 m

3. a) 467 g   **b)** £75

55 Perimeter and area

1. a) 34 cm, 60 cm² **b)** 6 cm, 90 cm² **c)** 6.25 cm, 56.5 cm²

2. 143 cm²

56 Compound shapes

1. perimeter = 44 cm, area = 101 cm²

2. perimeter = 84 cm, area = 369 cm²

3. perimeter = 32 cm, area = 48 cm²

57 Parallelograms

1. 153 cm²

2. a) perimeter = 130 cm   area = 392 cm²

  b) perimeter = 80 cm   area = 148.5 cm²

58 Triangles

1. a) 58.5 cm²

2. a) perimeter = 159 cm   area = 657 cm²

  b) perimeter = 59 cm   area = 100 cm²

3. 9 cm

59 Volumes of cuboids

1. a) 200 cm³   **b)** 284.375 cm³

2. 2,460.375 cm³   **3.** 326.2 cm³

60 Measurement problems

1. a) 90,420 cm²   **b)** 85,300 cm²

2. 675 cm³

3. 37 kg

GEOMETRY

61 2D shapes

1. a) equilateral
  b) isosceles
  c) scalene
  d) isosceles

2. a) kite (irregular)
  b) arrowhead (irregular)
  c) pentagon (regular)

3. rhombus

4. regular octagon

62 Angles

1. a) acute   **b)** reflex
  c) reflex   **d)** obtuse

2. a) 90° and 60°   **b)** 90° and 75°

3. a) 65°   **b)** 106°
  c) 129°

63 Angle problems

1. a) $a = 25°$ $b = 155°$ $c = 25°$
  b) $a = 75°$ $b = 105°$ $c = 75°$

2. $a = 60°$ $b = 60°$ $c = 120°$
  $d = 120°$ $e = 300°$ $f = 180°$

64 Circles

1. a) 18 cm   **b)** 86 cm   **c)** 16.5 cm

2. a) 0.44 m²   **b)** 72.2 cm²

3. a) circumference   **b)** chord   **c)** sector

4. 22.5 cm²

65 3D shapes

1. a) triangular prism **b)** sphere   **c)** cylinder   **d)** cone

2.

name of shape	number of faces	number of vertices	number of edges
cube	6	8	12
cuboid	6	8	12
tetrahedron	4	4	6
octahedron	8	6	12
triangular prism	5	6	9

66 Nets

1. the last net would not make a cube

2. a) triangular prism **b)** square-based pyramid **c)** cylinder

3.

67 Coordinates

1. A (4,2)   B (−5,4)   C (3, −1)
  D (5, 0)   E (−2, −4)   F (−1, −3)

2. The line is vertical as all the x-coordinates are the same.

3. Other coordinates could include:
  (−1, 1) (0, 2), (2, 4), (3, 5), (4, 6), (5, 7)

68 Translations

1. a) B (1, 1) C (7, −1)
  E (−7, −4) F (−1, −4) G (−1, −7)

  b)

B (2, 6) C (8, 4) D (−6, −2) E (−6, 1) F (0, 1) G (0, −2)

2. **a)** (−4, −3) (−4, 1) (1, 2)
   b) (−2, 1) (−2, 5) (3, 6)
   c) (−4, −7) (−4, −3)

69 Reflection

1. Check drawings and reflections carefully.
2. **a)** (−3, −3) (−1, −3) (−1, −1) (−3, −1)
   b) (3, 3) (1, 3) (1, 1) (3, 1)
3. **a)** (1, 2) (1, 4) (10, 4) (10, 2)
   b) (−1, −2) (−1, −4) (−10, −4) (−10, −2)

STATISTICS

70 Tables

1. **a)** Chatburn Road   **b)** 11   **c)** 75
   d) St Mark's   **e)** Ribble High   **f)** 14

71 Bar charts

1. **a)**

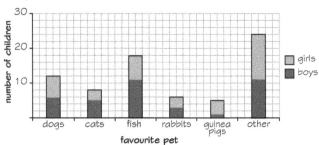

   b) 31   **c)** dogs and rabbits
   d) 35   **e)** 37   **f)** 25%

72 Reading pie charts

1. **a)** 24   **b)** 12
2. **a)** 3   **b)** 18
3. 3

73 Pie chart problems

1. **a)** 5   **b)** 20
   c) A quarter of the boys and a quarter of the girls like comedy films best. There are more boys than girls, so she is not correct. More boys like comedy best.
   d) 1   **e)** 91

74 Drawing pie charts

1. **a)**

favourite flavour of ice cream	number of children	angle of the slice
strawberry	8	96°
vanilla	3	36°
chocolate	15	180°
mint	4	48°

   b) 30
   c) Use a protractor to check the angles for all the sectors are correct.

75 Line graphs

1. **a)** 09:00   **b)** 13:00
   c) 6,000 m   **d)** 09:30
   e) 4.4 km   **f)** 11:00–11:45
   g) 1.6 km   **h)** 09:30–10:00

76 Mean

1. **a)** 4.5   **b)** 6.5   **c)** 20
2. £3.10
3. **a)** 17   **b)** 15   **c)** 21

Published by Pearson Education Limited, 80 Strand, London, WC2R 0RL.

www.pearsonschools.co.uk

Text © Pearson Education Limited 2016
Edited by Christine Vaughan
Typeset by Jouve India Private Limited
Produced by Elektra Media
Original illustrations © Pearson Education Limited 2016
Illustrated by Elektra Media
Cover illustration by Ana Albero

The right of Rachel Axten-Higgs to be identified as author of this work has been asserted by her in accordance with the Copyright, Designs and Patents Act 1988.

First published 2016

British Library Cataloguing in Publication Data
A catalogue record for this book is available from the British Library.

ISBN 978 1 292 14627 0